Capstone

Exemplary Lessons for **High School Economics**

Student Activities

National Council on Economic Education

This publication was made possible through funding from the Calvin K. Kazanjian Economics Foundation.

Authors

Jane S. Lopus
Professor of Economics and Director, Center for Economic Education
California State University, Hayward
Hayward, California

John S. Morton
Vice President for Program Development
National Council on Economic Education
Scottsdale, Arizona

Robert Reinke
Professor of Economics and Executive Director, South Dakota Council on Economic Education
University of South Dakota
Vermillion, South Dakota

Mark C. Schug
Professor of Curriculum and Instruction and Director, Center for Economic Education
University of Wisconsin-Milwaukee
Milwaukee, Wisconsin

Donald R. Wentworth
Professor of Economics and Director, Center for Economic Education
Pacific Lutheran University
Tacoma, Washington

Cover photos by: © Zoran Milich / Masterfile, © Ron Fehling / Masterfile, © David Muir / Masterfile, © Carl Valiquet / Masterfile and © Daryl Benson / Masterfile

ISBN: 1-56183-516-1

TABLE OF CONTENTS

Note: Lessons 8, 28, 30, 33, 34, 36, and 40 have no accompanying Student Activity.

Unit 5 The Visible Hand: The Role of Government in a Market Economy

Unit 6 The Macroeconomy

Unit 7 Markets Without Borders: The Global Economy

UNIT 1

THE ECONOMIC WAY OF THINKING

Unit 1, Lesson 1

Activity 1

Why Are We a Nation of Couch Potatoes?

Many people think that economics is as dry as dust and as remote as the moon. Is it really? Not at all. Economics asks you to consider problems in a mature, real-world sort of way. It gives you an intellectual edge in addressing problems. Its twists and turns are sometimes unexpected and sometimes fun.

Guide to Economic Reasoning

The key assumptions of economics may be stated variously and applied with different emphases, depending on the problem at hand. These principles can't do your thinking for you, but they provide you with a place to begin — a source of hunches to play out against the evidence, and a means of sorting the useful clues from the useless ones.

This **Guide to Economic Reasoning** focuses on six principles:

1. People *choose*.
2. People's choices involve *costs*.
3. People respond to *incentives* in predictable ways.
4. People create economic *systems* that influence individual choices and incentives.
5. People gain when they *trade voluntarily*.
6. People's choices have *consequences that lie in the future*.

To get familiar with these principles, think about how they might apply to the mystery of why the United States is becoming a nation of couch potatoes. We know that many Americans admire people who are fit and trim. We also know that not exercising enough and eating too much can cause a number of health problems including cancer, diabetes, and heart disease. So, why do Americans increasingly exercise too little and eat too much? And what might economics have to do with the question?

Your first response might be that Americans are lazy. Is this the best explanation? Let's work through the principles of the **Guide** to see what light they shed on the problem.

1. People *choose*.

This principle may seem to state the obvious, but it is meant to emphasize two important meanings. First, people do in fact make choices. Think about how often you hear people say that, in one situation or another, they had "no choice" but to act as they did. In this respect, young people and adults are much alike. Both are prone to deny that they are making choices when that is exactly what they are doing. In some cases, at least, both are prone to explain their actions as matters of necessity — perhaps necessity imposed by others.

Second, economists claim that, in making choices, people are rational. They are rational in that *they seek by their choices to obtain the best possible combination of costs and benefits.* To put it in other words: In choosing, people are *economizing*. They are trying to make the best decisions they can under the circumstances. The circumstances include the relative importance of the decision, what the person making the decision knows, what it will cost to learn more, and how much time there is in which to decide.

What does all this have to do with Americans becoming couch potatoes? Using economic reasoning, we assume that behavior related to exercise and diet is the result of personal choice regarding several matters, including work and the use of leisure time.

2. People's choices involve *costs*.

Decisions come with costs. Always. This is clear enough in the case of decisions to buy something. But the costs that come with decisions are not always dollar costs. Deciding to chat on the phone a while longer with a friend might seem to be free. But the cost in that case might be, for example, not doing your homework or missing a favorite television show.

While there are many kinds of cost, economists stress the importance of *opportunity cost*. In any decision, the opportunity cost is the person's second-best choice. It is not every alternative not selected. After all, the list of alternatives in a given case is endless. Of all the possibilities, the opportunity cost is the second-best alternative — the one you would have chosen next.

Do costs apply to decisions about exercise? Of course. Imagine that you have just returned home from school. You are a little tired. You could pull on your running shoes and go for a two-mile jog. Or you could sink into your favorite chair, reach for the remote, and watch your favorite after-school television show. You choose to watch television. You traded off jogging for watching television. The opportunity cost was jogging not jogged. Exercise is not free.

Do choices about diet entail costs and trade-offs? Of course. Imagine that you have joined a group of friends to eat out at your favorite fast-food restaurant. You consider two items from the menu, a tasty salad or your favorite double cheeseburger with mushrooms, bacon, and a special sauce. You choose the salad. Your opportunity cost is the double cheeseburger — a big sacrifice for many of us!

continued on next page   

According to two prominent economists, the cost of exercising has increased recently. What might this mean? Not long ago, and throughout most of our history, work in the United States was often strenuous and dangerous. Many jobs involved plowing, hauling, shoveling, climbing, digging, lifting, chopping, stooping, handling large animals, fishing from small boats in heavy seas, and so on. In doing work of this sort, Americans were, in effect, paid to exercise. Exercise came with the job, as a sort of fringe benefit.

In the United States today, work has changed. Most work now entails little exercise. For millions of Americans, work means sitting at a desk staring into a computer screen, tapping on a keyboard, talking on a cell phone, and attending meetings. Instead of *getting paid to exercise*, many people in sedentary jobs must *pay to exercise* — spending money and leisure time to exercise at health clubs, for example. The increased cost in time and money discourages many Americans from exercising or decreases the time they spend doing it.

3. People respond to *incentives* in predictable ways.

Incentives are rewards. One powerful incentive is money. It is a powerful incentive because it can be exchanged for other things that people want. But not all incentives are monetary. Another sort of incentive has to do with the satisfaction that comes from doing the right thing. Examples abound. Many people perform acts of kindness that involve no monetary rewards. They volunteer to donate blood and vital organs, they pick up trash in a park or along the highway, they show up to vote on election day. Some people — including police officers and fire fighters — risk their lives daily for reasons that go beyond the salaries they earn.

In one sense, however, these acts of kindness and civic virtue can also be explained by economic principles. Such acts reflect self-interest, economists might say, not selfishness. The self-interest is the interest some people have in living a certain sort of life.

How do incentives bear on the case of the burgeoning couch potatoes? Americans must be responding to incentives. Consider two. First, the price of food acts as an incentive. Technological changes have greatly lowered food prices. This means that the cost of calories, including excess calories, has decreased. The decrease in cost amounts to an incentive, encouraging people to eat more than they otherwise would.

Improvements in passive entertainment provide a second incentive. Many Americans now have hundreds of choices for television viewing. New programs are constantly being invented, tested, and accepted or rejected by audiences. Computer games also are attractive to many people. For some, these games are nearly impossible to put down. The fun people derive from passive entertainment acts as an incentive, encouraging them to remain firmly rooted to their couches or desk chairs.

4. People create economic *systems* that influence individual decisions.

Economic behavior occurs in a climate of rules, formal and informal. The "rules of the game" influence the choices people make in particular cases. Rules often act as incentives. Tax laws, for example, influence people's behavior. If a city government places a heavy tax on the width of buildings, tall, narrow buildings soon begin popping up. If a state government places a large tax on savings accounts, people soon begin keeping less money in those accounts.

How might the "rules of the game" influence the behavior of couch potatoes? The American economy is a relatively open and free system. It changes and grows as technology and consumer tastes change. People are rewarded for creating new goods and services and new ways of supplying them to consumers.

The historic shift from manufacturing jobs to service jobs in the United States has changed our typical levels of physical activity. Most service jobs involve light work, physically, and some jobs in the service sector pay very well. Thus, our economic system has created conditions in which people now are likely to take jobs that are not physically demanding.

The rules of the American economic system encourage businesses to respond to consumer demand. Many consumers are obviously interested in making life easier at home. Businesses have responded by producing all sorts of labor-saving devices: power lawn mowers, snow and leaf blowers, dishwashers, washing machines and dryers, electric stoves, TV remotes, gas and electric furnaces, freezers, vacuum cleaners, prepared foods, microwaves, and so on. But in the drive for ease and convenience there is an unintended consequence. The devices that save us time and effort also reduce the amount of physical work done at home. At home and at work, then, our economic system allows people to substitute technology for physical effort.

5. People gain when they *trade voluntarily*.

"Voluntary" here refers to a lack of coercion. "Your money or your life!" does not describe an instance of voluntary trade. "Gain" refers to money gains, of course, but also to other benefits. Examples of voluntary trade are everywhere. Purchasing a movie ticket, filling a car with gas, buying a stock — all involve instances of voluntary trade in which people exchange something they value less for something they value more.

continued on next page   

What does voluntary trade have to do with exercise and diet? Exchanges involving employment rarely highlight exercise and diet as top priorities. Instead, people understand that service jobs are likely to be safe and healthful in a physical sense, involving little wear and tear on the body. Many people are willing to trade their labor for the income and benefits offered by employers in the service sector. They recognize correctly that they are likely to live longer and work longer as a result. Both the employer and the employee benefit from such an exchange.

People gain when they trade voluntarily, but this general principle does not mean that people can't make mistakes. Things can go wrong, as anybody who has ever made a bad decision knows. While the benefits of safer jobs are clear, safer jobs come with problems of their own. The desk job that ensures a worker against threats of muscle strain and frostbite may also add to the worker's risk of gaining weight.

In purchasing food, people also engage in voluntary trade — sometimes more than they should. Grocery store owners and restaurant owners are happy to oblige. In this sense, all parties are better off as a result of the exchanges they make. But here too people obviously make mistakes — eating more today, perhaps, while telling themselves that they will reduce their intake and start exercising tomorrow.

6. People's choices have *consequences that lie in the future.*

Despite messages from advertisers urging all of us to "live for today," many people work hard at living for tomorrow. At least they give thought to tomorrow as they strive to make decisions that will benefit them in the future. For example, people tend to care for cars they own better than the cars they sometimes rent. Car owners have a long-term interest in caring for their cars, since maintenance bills and resale values are affected by the quality of care owners provide. Similarly, many homeowners care for their homes more lovingly than they cared for the apartments they once rented — again because they have a long-term interest in their homes' quality and market value.

Overall, the shift toward work that is physically less demanding and less dangerous has made Americans better off. The same economic and technological progress that has boosted Americans' standard of living has made work more sedentary. For many Americans it also has made life outside the workplace more interesting. While workers are less often "paid" to exercise today, they also are less vulnerable to the dangers and costly injuries their parents and grandparents often faced on the job. In this sense, people have traded thinness to live longer, healthier, and more interesting lives than ever before. This is not to say that people want to be overweight, but they do seem to prefer it to the alternatives.

The negative consequences of being a couch potato, however, have also begun to influence people in their views of the future. People are joining health clubs in record numbers. People are trying to reduce the cost of exercise by doing more of it on the job — by forming exercise groups at work, for example, or by avoiding elevators and taking walks during breaks, or by parking at remote lots and walking or bicycling into the office. In an economic system of choices, costs, and consequences, one thing does lead to another in this way.

Questions for Discussion

A. What is the economic view of choice?

____

____

____

B. How do choices influence people in respect to exercise and diet?

____

____

____

C. What is an opportunity cost?

____

____

____

D. How does opportunity cost influence people in their decisions about exercise and diet?

____

____

____

E. What is an incentive?

____

____

____

continued on next page

F. Why is money such an attractive incentive?

G. What incentives influence people in their decisions about exercise and diet?

H. Why are the rules of the economic system important?

I. How do the rules of the economic system influence people in their decisions about exercise and diet?

J. What is voluntary trade?

K. How does voluntary trade influence people in their decisions about exercise and diet?

L. What does it mean to say that people's choices have future consequences?

M. How do future consequences influence people in their decisions about exercise and diet?

N. Solve the mystery: Why do an increasing number of Americans, the same people who admire the slender look so often featured in the media, exercise too little and eat too much?

Unit 1, Lesson 2

Activity 1

Which Examples Illustrate Scarcity?

Directions: Mark an "S" at the end of the statement if you think the item is scarce. Mark "NS" if the item is not scarce.

A. Old economics textbooks collected in a bookcase near the teacher's desk with a sign that says "Free books, take as many as you want." The books have been there for three years. ____

B. Old economics textbooks collected in a bookcase near the teacher's desk with a sign that says "Free books, take as many as you want." Another sign posted in the hallway says "$10 paid for any recycled textbook. Bring books to the Principal's office." ____

C. One economics textbook, five students who wish to do well in the economics course, and an important test in class the next day. ____

D. One economics textbook, five students who are not taking economics, and an important test in the economics class the next day. ____

E. Petroleum in Japan, a country without its own oil fields and without oil reserves. ____

F. Petroleum in Saudi Arabia, a country with many oil fields and oil reserves. _____

Unit 1, Lesson 2

Activity 2

Are People Treating Scarce Resources as Scarce?

Directions: Mark an "S" at the end of the statement if you think the item is scarce. Mark a "NS" if the item is not scarce.

A. Water fountains in Rome flow continuously with water carried by viaducts from the Italian mountains. People walking in Rome quench their thirst by drinking from the fountains. But most of the water flows into the street and down the drains to a river that passes through the city. ____

B. At closing time, restaurants in the United States are required to throw away all uneaten food. To meet health standards for food preparation and the safety of consumers, the food cannot be stored for use the next day. Also, the law prohibits restaurant employees from giving the food to the poor or dispersing it to local food banks. ____

C. Oxygen is taken from the air and stored in containers. When divers wish to stay underwater for long periods of time, they purchase container-stored oxygen and breathe from it during their underwater activities. ____

D. Pebbles are taken from a beach to build a walkway in a homeowner's lawn. No one else wants the pebbles. The pebbles are not necessary for the lake's ecosystem or animal habitat. ____

E. A farmer has a water irrigation contract that requires the water user to use the entire allocation of water to water crops, whether or not all the water is needed for crop irrigation. If the farmer does not use all the water, he or she will receive a smaller allocation next year. ____

Unit 1, Lesson 3

Activity 1

Survival

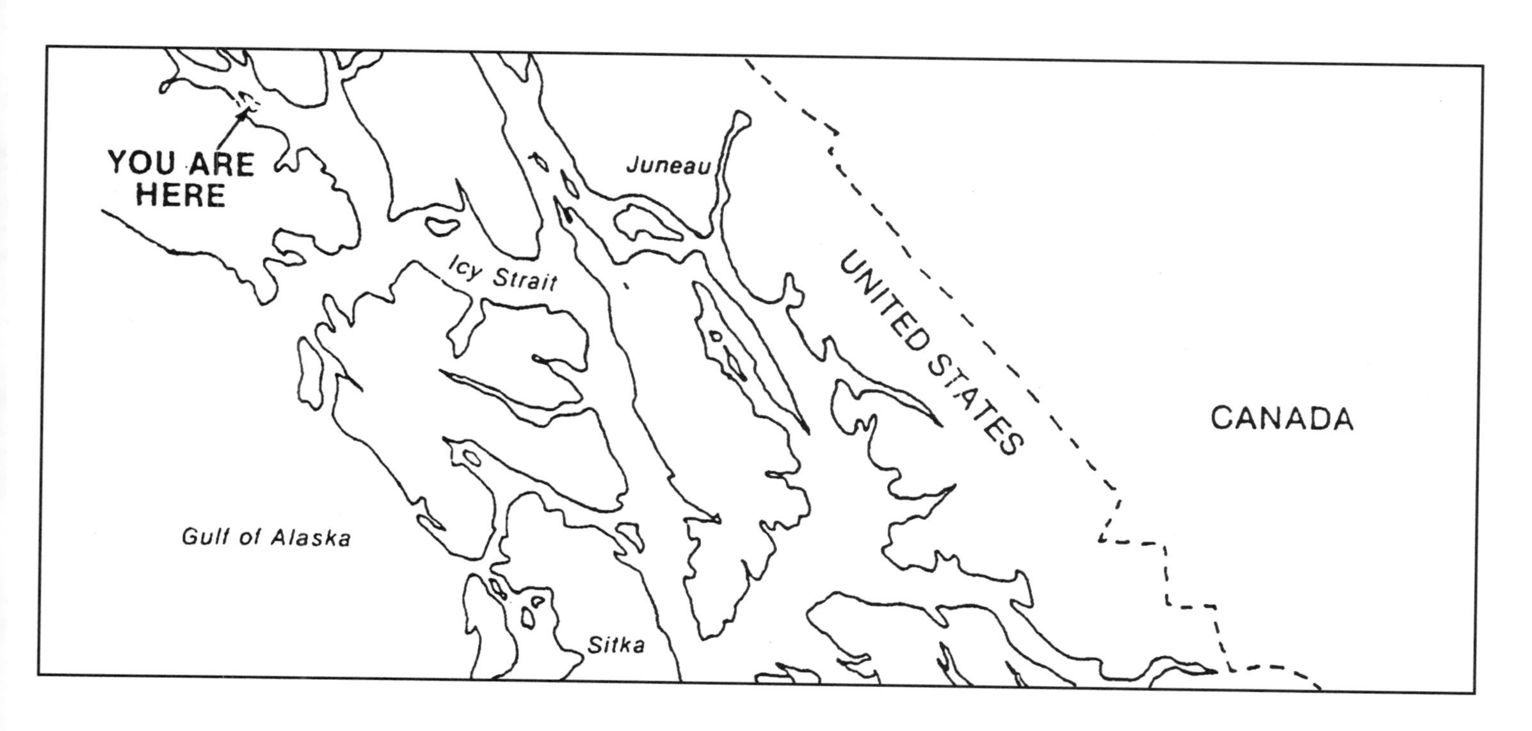

ENVIRONMENT

Land

sandy & rocky beach
rough cliffs
mountainous interior
thick forest with Douglas fir and Sitka spruce trees

Climate

mild summers
frequent rain showers
morning & evening fog
changeable weather

Wildlife

deer & rabbits
seagulls & eagles
fish & clams

SALVAGED EQUIPMENT

1 compass (no radio)

2 rain ponchos

1 book of matches

2 knives

3 life preservers

2 paddles

1 small axe

wet clothing (what you are wearing)

continued on next page  

Unit 1, Lesson 3

Activity 1

Survival (cont.)

Write your survival plan below. As you develop your survival plan, consider the following questions.

1. What will you produce?
2. How will you make it?
3. How will you share it?

Unit 1, Lesson 4

Activity 1

Alternatives and Choices

A world of scarcity forces people to choose among competing alternatives. Naturally, people try to pick the alternative that provides the greatest benefit at the lowest cost. Sometimes alternatives have such high costs that we don't even consider them seriously.

Alternatives An alternative is one of many different actions that we might take in a given situation. If we have $20 to spend, one alternative might be to buy a DVD; another alternative might be to buy pizza for friends. If we are hiking and meet a grizzly bear on the path ahead, one alternative might be to make ugly faces at it in the hope that it will run away; another alternative might be to get out of the area as quickly as possible.

Choices A choice is the course of action we take when faced with a set of alternatives. Some people with $20 to spend will choose to buy the DVD, others the pizza, still others might choose a different alternative altogether. In the hiking example, not many people would choose the face-making alternative because of its likelihood of failure.

Directions: Read each of the cases below. Identify the alternatives and the anticipated costs and benefits for each situation. Indicate which alternative you would choose by putting a check (✔) next to it. Choice Grid 1 is completed for you as an example.

1. Ashley desperately wanted to attend a concert with her friends. Unfortunately, she could not get a ticket for the night on which her friends were going to the concert. She said she had no choice but to stay home with her family and watch TV. Did Ashley have a choice?

CHOICE GRID 1

Alternatives	*Possible Costs*	*Possible Benefits*
Stay home and watch TV	Miss the concert	Watch TV with family
Go to concert alone	Less enjoyment/ not sharing the same experience	Enjoy the concert
Study homework	Less exciting than concert	Improve school performance

2. Samantha Marsh operates Sam's Spicy Subs & Wraps, a sandwich stand near Jefferson High School. Every day she sells her special sandwiches and wraps to loyal high school customers who flock to the stand during lunch hour. Recently, Sam raised her prices by $1 per sandwich. Several customers protested. They said the sandwiches now cost more than buying lunch at the burger shop up the street, or—worse yet—more than buying lunch at school. Sam explained that her costs had gone up because of new license fees and regulations imposed by the City Health Department. She had no choice but to increase her prices, she said.

CHOICE GRID 2

Alternatives	*Possible Costs*	*Possible Benefits*

3. Mr. Otto Wurker owns a factory that supplies airbags and global positioning systems (GPS) to U.S. automobile manufacturers. Otto has fallen on tough times. Imports from Europe and Asia have cut into sales of U.S. cars, and many of Otto's friends and employees have been laid off. Looking over the almost-empty factory, he says to the visiting U.S. senators who are touring this economically depressed area, "America has no choice: we must restrict imports of foreign cars and trucks to save U.S. jobs."

CHOICE GRID 3

Alternatives	*Possible Costs*	*Possible Benefits*

continued on next page   

Unit 1, Lesson 5

Activity 1

Quiz

Do not write on this quiz sheet. Mark all your answers on Activity 2 or 3, the First or Second Answer Sheet only!

1. Making a choice means:
   A. Deciding among many possibilities.
   B. Not thinking of future consequences.
   C. Being able to get everything.
   D. Considering your daily horoscope.

2. People throughout the world usually make choices:
   A. Impulsively—choosing quickly without much thought.
   B. Generously—thinking of the needs of others.
   C. Randomly—leaving the outcome up to chance.
   D. Purposefully—considering costs and benefits.

3. An incentive is:
   A. A fictitious animal that exists only in fables and fairy tales.
   B. A sacrifice above and beyond the call of duty.
   C. A reward you wish to receive.
   D. A fancy dessert that you can order at elegant restaurants.

4. How are incentives related to choices?
   A. Incentives motivate people to make certain types of choices.
   B. Incentives rarely influence personal choices.
   C. Incentives make it difficult to predict what choices people will make.
   D. Incentives have nothing to do with choices.

5. High school football players turn out for practice on a daily basis; they endure tough physical workouts and get sore muscles and bruised bodies. The personal incentive for choosing to do this most likely would be:
   A. Money, profit, and financial well-being.
   B. Acclaim, stature, and prestige.
   C. Safety, insurance, and security.
   D. Toil, pain, and hardship.

6. A rule is:
   A. A greeting, a beginning, or an introduction.
   B. A country, a state, or a nation.
   C. A law, a guideline, or a regulation.
   D. A shape, a size, or a volume.

7. How are rules related to incentives?
   A. Rules are designed to eliminate incentives.
   B. Rules influence personal incentives.
   C. Rules are made to enforce incentives.
   D. Rules have nothing to do with incentives.

8. Joe is a salesperson for a company that makes DVDs. Company rules allow Joe to obtain DVDs each month, and he is paid $10 for every DVD he orders from the company. He can keep the money even if he doesn't sell all the DVDs. Joe's incentive is profit. He wants to make as much money as possible. Joe probably will choose to:
   A. Obtain fewer DVDs than he thinks he can sell.
   B. Obtain exactly as many DVDs as he thinks he can actually sell.
   C. Obtain more DVDs than he thinks he can sell.
   D. Find a different way to make a living.

continued on next page

9. Recently, Joe's company changed its rules. The company now allows Joe to obtain a certain number of DVDs each month and keep $10 for each DVD he sells. Also, the new rules state that Joe must pay the company for every DVD he obtains but does not sell by the end of the month. Joe's incentive is profit. He still wants to make as much money as possible. Joe will most likely choose to:

   A. Obtain fewer DVDs than he thinks he can sell.

   B. Obtain exactly as many DVDs as he thinks he can actually sell.

   C. Obtain more DVDs than he thinks he can sell.

   D. Retire.

10. People usually trade with each other when:

   A. They don't know what to expect from making a trade.

   B. They think they will be worse off after making a trade.

   C. They predict that the costs of trading will be greater than the benefits.

   D. They feel they will be better off from making a trade.

Unit 1, Lesson 5

Activity 2

First Answer Sheet

Name____

Score = Total Number Correct ____________ Grade: _________

1.______________

2.______________

3.______________

4.______________

5.______________

6.______________

7.______________

8.______________

9.______________

10.______________

Unit 1, Lesson 5

Activity 3

Second Answer Sheet

Name____

Score = Total Number Correct ____________ Grade: _________

1.____________

2.____________

3.____________

4.____________

5.____________

6.____________

7.____________

8.____________

9.____________

10.____________

Unit 1, Lesson 5

Activity 4

How Rules Influence Economic Activity

Directions: Below are five examples of rules related to economic activity. For each rule, decide whether it would encourage or discourage economic activity. (Note: Some of the examples involve important religious beliefs or cultural values. The purpose of this activity is not to judge those beliefs or values. The question in each case is whether the rule would encourage or discourage economic activity.)

A. In Afghanistan, under Taliban rule, women could not go to school, hold jobs, or move around in public without an escort.

Encourage_____

Discourage_____

B. In Russia, when it was part of the former Soviet Union, managers of nail factories were rewarded for producing large numbers of nails. No reward was given for making nails in different sizes.

Encourage_____

Discourage_____

C. In the United States, if the water in a river provides the habitat for an endangered species, the water cannot be used to irrigate crops, create electricity, or water livestock.

Encourage_____

Discourage_____

D. In many parts of India, cows are considered sacred, and people are not allowed to use beef as a food.

Encourage_____

Discourage_____

E. In Argentina, beef is considered an important food source, and Argentine cows are sold to people around the world.

Encourage_____

Discourage_____

UNIT 2

THE INVISIBLE HAND AT WORK

Lesson 6

Activity 1 Why Did Communism Collapse?

Lesson 7

Activity 1 How to Play a Silver Market

Activity 2 Student Score Sheet for a Silver Market

Activity 3 Supply and Demand Schedules for Silver

Lesson 9

Activity 1 How Many Hours Are You Willing to Work?

Activity 2 The Amazing Farmer Jones

Lesson 10

Activity 1 Equilibrium Prices and Equilibrium Quantities

Lesson 11

Activity 1 Do Prices Matter to Consumers?

Lesson 12

Activity 1 Picturing and Calculating Elasticity

Lesson 13

Activity 1 I, Pencil

Activity 2 How Markets Allocate Resources

Lesson 14

Activity 1 What Will Happen If?

Unit 2, Lesson 6

Activity 1

Why Did Communism Collapse?

A communist economic system is one in which the state owns and controls the means of production and distribution. For much of the twentieth century, communism and socialism dominated economic thinking in many nations of the world. Among these nations was the Soviet Union, where the Soviet Communist Party controlled the government and the economy, and sought to expand its power to control other regions in the world as well. The United States and other nations opposed Soviet expansion during a period known as the Cold War. In the 1950s, it appeared that the Soviet Union might win the Cold War. Soviet Premier Nikita Khruschev stated in 1957, "We will bury you." But the Soviet Union collapsed abruptly in 1991. What explains the demise of the Soviet Union?

In approaching this question, we will make use of the **Guide to Economic Reasoning:**

1. People choose.
2. People's choices involve costs.
3. People respond to incentives in predictable ways.
4. People create economic systems that influence individual choices and incentives.
5. People gain when they trade voluntarily.
6. People's choices have consequences that lie in the future.

With these principles in mind, let's examine the answers to the True/False questions about our mystery.

A. For much of the twentieth century, nearly one-third of the world's population lived under communism or socialism.

True. The Soviet Union, shortly after the October Revolution of 1917, abolished private land ownership and established worker control (exercised by Communist Party authorities) over many industries and banks. This pattern was followed in varying degrees by many other nations. China, Vietnam, North Korea, and Cuba all became communist nations. After World War II, India and several newly independent nations of Africa opted for a dominant governmental role in the ownership of productive resources. Private ownership — being able to own property and use it freely for one's own economic benefit — was widely disregarded as a key "rule of the game." (Principle 4)

B. The Soviet Union worked from the premise that only government planners could provide for the overall economic well-being of Soviet society.

True. In 1928, under the leadership of Joseph Stalin, Soviet economic and political leaders established Five-Year Plans that set goals for what (and how many) goods and services should be produced nationwide. These plans also specified how goods and services were to be distributed.

In market economies, individuals are regarded as having the best information for making such decisions. Individual farmers in South Dakota, for example, have much better information regarding what to plant, when they should plant, and when they should harvest than would officials in the Washington, D.C., Department of Agriculture. (Principle 4)

C. In a market economy, prices send important information to producers and consumers regarding the relative value of goods and services.

True. In a market economy, prices reflect the value of a good to the society and the cost of making the good. People in households and businesses react to prices when they decide what to buy or sell. As a result, prices act as incentives for producers. They guide individual decisions that, in many cases, benefit all of us by encouraging the best use of scarce resources. (Principles 3 and 4)

D. In command economies, prices are controlled by the government.

True. In the Soviet Union, the "rules of the game" authorized government officials to decide what quantities of goods and services would be produced, and to set prices. As a result, how much the system produced had little to do with consumer wants. Prices did not reflect the true value of the goods and services that were being produced. Households and industries were given false signals about the relative value of goods and services. Thus some goods and services were over-produced while others were under-produced. Vast amounts of waste and environmental destruction were among the chief results. (Principles 3 and 4)

Unit 2, Lesson 7

Activity 1

How to Play A Silver Market

Read these instructions carefully. They will help you make money through smart trading. The goal for both buyers and sellers is to make a profit.

Buyers

1. Each buyer will receive only one card at a time.
2. Each buyer will have only one buy order at a time. It will say, "You are authorized to **BUY** one ounce of silver, paying as **little** as possible. If you pay more than $___ per ounce, you lose money." The exact price will be written on each card.
3. When the round starts, try to buy at the lowest price you can. You may, if necessary, buy at a price higher than the price on your Buy card in order to obtain your silver. As soon as you have bought an ounce of silver, record the trade on your score sheet. Then turn the Buy card in and get another buy order. If you do not buy silver during a round, return your buy order after the round is finished.
4. Remember that if you buy below the price on your Buy card, you make money. Think of it as a profit for the buyer. If you buy above the price on your card, you lose money.

Sellers

1. Each seller will receive only one card at a time.
2. Each seller will have only one sell order at a time. It will say, "You are authorized to **SELL** one ounce of silver for as **much** as possible. If you accept less than $___ per ounce, you lose money." The exact price will be written on each card.
3. When the round starts, try to sell your silver at the highest price you can. You may, if necessary, sell at a price lower than the price on your Sell card in order to get rid of your silver. As soon as you have sold your silver, record the trade on your score sheet. Then go to the teacher or recorder to report the selling price and get another Sell card. If you do not sell silver during a round, return your sell order after the round is finished.
4. **Reminder**: As the seller, you must report the price of the trade to the recorder. The buyer does not have to do this. Information depends on you, the seller.
5. Remember that if you sell above the price on your Sell card, you make a profit. If you sell below the price on your card, you have a loss.

The Market in Action

1. When the teacher says, "The market is open," sellers and buyers should meet and try to agree on a price for one ounce of silver. Any buyer can talk with any seller.
2. The goal for both buyers and sellers is to make as much money as they can. The buyers do this by buying silver for a lower price than the one shown on their cards. The sellers make money by selling for a higher price than the price shown on their cards.
3. All students are free to make as many trades in a round as time permits.
4. Every time a seller reports an agreement to the recorder, it will be entered on the Class Tally Sheet. Watch the tally sheet so that you will know what prices are being paid.
5. As soon as buyers and sellers receive new cards during a round, they should return to the marketplace and try to make another deal.

Unit 2, Lesson 7

Activity 2

Student Score Sheet for A Silver Market

HOW TO USE THE SCORE SHEET

Use this score sheet to keep track of your progress during the simulation. Tally your gains and losses by taking the difference between the dollar value of one ounce of silver as stated on your card and the dollar value of the deal you made. If you are a buyer, you gain whenever you buy at a **LOWER** price than the price shown on your card. If you buy at a higher price, you suffer a loss. If you are a seller, you gain whenever you sell at a **HIGHER** price than the price shown on your card. At a lower price, you suffer a loss. When your teacher instructs you to do so, total your gains and losses and write them in the designated spaces.

Circle One: **BUYER** **SELLER**

Transaction	Price on Card	Trading Price	Gain	Loss	Cumulative Profit or Loss
1					
2					
3					
4					
5					
Total for Round 1					
1					
2					
3					
4					
5					
Total for Round 2					
1					
2					
3					
4					
5					
Total for Round 3					
1					
2					
3					
4					
5					
Total for Round 4					
Grand Total					

Unit 2, Lesson 7

Activity 3

Supply and Demand Schedules for Silver

SUPPLY SCHEDULE:

In the following table, the supply schedule in the third column equals the cumulative number of ounces of silver available for sale at the price indicated. The cumulative total is found by adding in the second column all the ounces produced at a given price and at all lower prices. (Obviously, any producer willing to sell an ounce at a price of $3.50 will still be willing to sell that ounce at a higher price.)

Price	*Number of Sellers Willing to Sell 1 Ounce of Silver at the Price Indicated or at a Lower Price*	*Supply Schedule*
$3.50	4 sellers = 4 oz.	4
$3.70	6 sellers = 6 oz.	10
$3.90	6 sellers = 6 oz.	16
$4.10	4 sellers = 4 oz.	20
$4.30	4 sellers = 4 oz.	24
$4.50	2 sellers = 2 oz.	26
$4.70	2 sellers = 2 oz.	28
$4.90	2 sellers = 2 oz.	30
$5.10	2 sellers = 2 oz.	32

DEMAND SCHEDULE:

In the following table, the demand schedule in the third column equals the cumulative number of ounces of silver buyers would be willing and able to buy at the price indicated. The cumulative total is found by adding in the second column all the ounces purchased at a given price and at all higher prices. (Obviously, any consumer willing to buy an ounce at a price of $5.30 will still be willing to buy that ounce at a lower price.)

Price	*Number of Buyers Willing to Buy 1 Ounce of Silver at the Price Indicated or at a Higher Price*	*Demand Schedule*
$5.30	4 buyers = 4 oz.	4
$5.10	4 buyers = 6 oz.	8
$4.90	4 buyers = 6 oz.	12
$4.70	4 buyers = 4 oz.	16
$4.50	4 buyers = 4 oz.	20
$4.30	4 buyers = 2 oz.	24
$4.10	2 buyers = 2 oz.	26
$3.90	2 buyers = 2 oz.	28
$3.70	2 buyers = 2 oz.	30
$3.50	2 buyers = 2 oz.	32

Use the information above to plot the supply and demand schedules on the graph provided at the end of this Activity. Label your graph and answer the following questions.

A. What is the relationship between the amount of silver people want to buy and the price? ______________________

____

B. What is the relationship between the amount of silver people want to sell and the price? ______________________

____

C. What is the equilibrium or market-clearing price on this graph? __________
What is the quantity traded at that price? __________

D. Were more trades made at this price in the simulation than at any other price? ___________

E. Why do you think all trades were not made at the equilibrium or market-clearing price?

____

____

F. How did prices change as you played additional rounds of the simulation?

____

____

continued on next page ●  

Unit 2, Lesson 7

Activity 3 (cont.)

A Silver Market

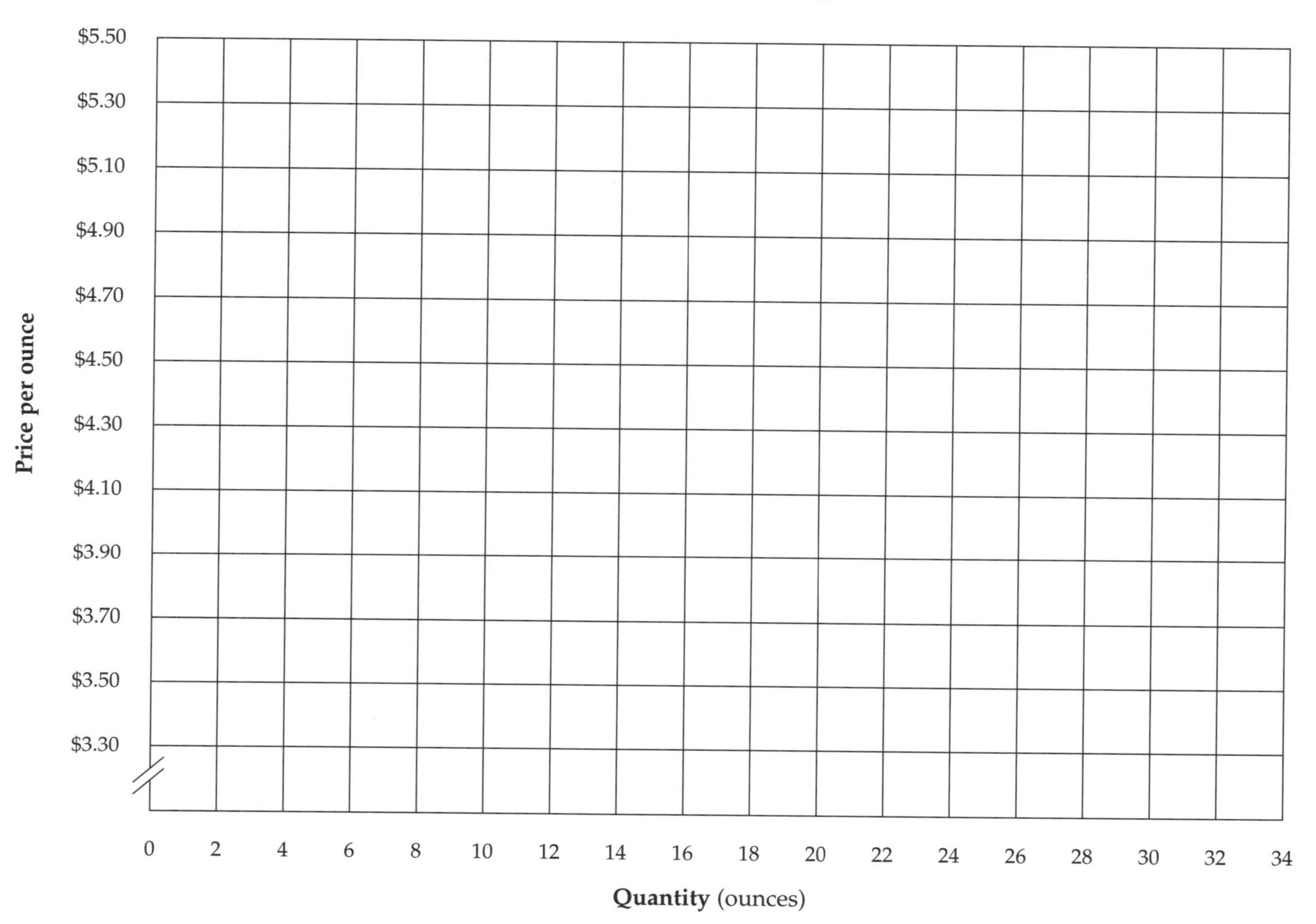

Unit 2, Lesson 9

Activity 1

How Many Hours Are You Willing to Work?

You have decided that you need to earn more money. You are considering applying for a part-time job. Describe the abilities you have that you think will influence the wage rate employers will offer you. Include knowledge, attitudes, and skills.

Knowledge	Attitudes	Skills
______________	______________	______________
______________	______________	______________
______________	______________	______________
______________	______________	______________

List the number of hours that you are willing to work per week at each of the hourly rates of pay in the column below. Assume a seven-day week, and remember that you must still attend school.

Hourly pay	Hours willing to work
$1.00	______________
$5.00	______________
$7.00	______________
$10.00	______________
$15.00	______________
$20.00	______________
$25.00	______________
$100.00	______________

Unit 2, Lesson 9

Activity 2

The Amazing Farmer Jones

There is a new look at Beth's Café in Corntown, South Dakota. While the café hasn't changed in appearance, the people who come in for their morning coffee sure have. Gone are the days when most of the customers wore bib overalls and their favorite tractor or seed caps and talked about rain, drought, and cattle prices.

Today, although most of the faces are the same, the customers at Beth's Café wear business casual, Gateway caps, construction aprons, or service uniforms. Many of them carry cell phones, and some wear the smiles of easy-going retired people. The discussion topics have changed from falling prices for grain and cattle to opportunities in the equities markets and the latest high-tech company to locate in town.

One retired farmer brings in a newspaper clipping that describes the Maize Craze. "What in the world is this all about?" he asks his old friend, Farmer Jones. Farmer Jones, one of the few farmers left in Beth's Café, explains: "Oh, that is the best use of my corn."

Some of the farmers are adjusting to low prices for grain by seeking alternative uses for their cropland. Some have left their fields full of grain for bird habitat, particularly for pheasants, while others have designed field-corn mazes for the tourists. The maze idea requires that farmers design the maze before planting and then thin the plants early in the season while the plants are still small. Although this reduces the per-acre yield, it yields other benefits. The Maize Craze has spurred the development of Maize Daze in some communities. These events attract many visitors, and the visitors shop in local stores, eat in local restaurants, and stay in local motels. In some communities, the local businesses pay farmers to create mazes. Also, farmers charge fees to people who want to enter their mazes. Farmer Jones says that his maze has really brought in the money. The Maize Craze, he thinks, will make farming profitable once again.

When the coffee break is over, one ex-farmer says as he leaves Beth's, "Maybe I will dust off my old John Deere cap and try farming one more time."

QUESTIONS FOR DISCUSSION

A. Why did so many farmers leave farming to go into other careers?

____

____

____

B. When many producers leave a market (as in the case of farming), what is likely to happen to the quantity produced at any given price?

____

____

____

Unit 2, Lesson 10

Activity 1

Equilibrium Prices and Equilibrium Quantities

Below is a table showing the demand for Frisbees and the supply of Frisbees. Plot these data on the axes provided. Label the demand curve "D" and the supply curve "S." Then answer the questions that follow.

Demand for and Supply of Frisbees

Price ($ per Frisbee)	Quantity Demanded (millions of Frisbees)	Quantity Supplied (millions of Frisbees)
$1.00	300	100
$2.00	250	150
$3.00	200	200
$4.00	150	250
$5.00	100	300

Plotting Demand for and Supply of Frisbees

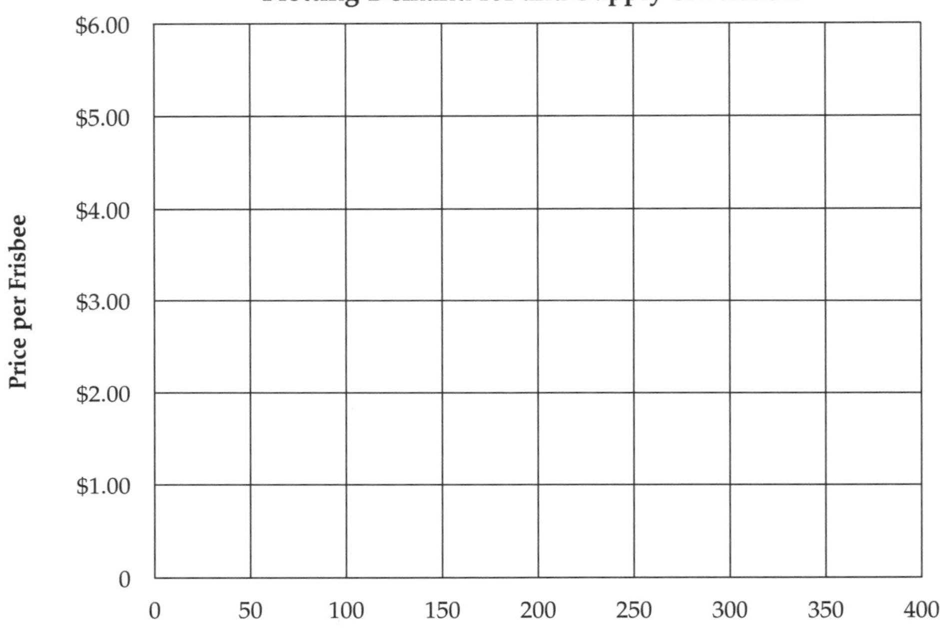

Fill in the answer blanks or cross out the incorrect words in parentheses.

A. Under these conditions, competitive market forces would tend to establish an equilibrium price of $__________ per Frisbee and an equilibrium quantity of __________ million Frisbees.

B. If the price currently prevailing on the market is $4.00 per Frisbee, buyers would want to buy __________ million Frisbees and sellers would want to sell __________ million Frisbees. Under these conditions, there would be a *(shortage/surplus)* of __________ million Frisbees. Competitive market forces would tend to cause the price to *(increase/decrease)* to a price of $__________ per Frisbee.

C. At this new price, buyers would now want to buy __________ million Frisbees, and sellers would now want to sell __________ million Frisbees. Because of this change in *(price/underlying conditions)*, the *(demand/quantity demanded)* changed by __________ million Frisbees, and the *(supply/quantity supplied)* changed by __________ million Frisbees.

continued on next page 

D. If the price currently prevailing on the market is $2.00 per Frisbee, buyers would want to buy __________ million Frisbees and sellers would want to sell __________ million Frisbees. Under these conditions, there would be a *(shortage/surplus)* of __________ million Frisbees. Competitive market forces would tend to cause the price to *(increase/decrease)* to a price of $__________ per Frisbee.

E. At this new price, buyers would now want to buy __________ million Frisbees, and sellers would now want to sell __________ million Frisbees. Because of this change in *(price/underlying conditions)*, the *(demand/quantity demanded)* changed by __________ million Frisbees, and the *(supply/quantity supplied)* changed by __________ million Frisbees.

F. Now suppose that an increase in the cost of plastic used to make Frisbees causes the supply curve to change as follows:

Change in Supply of Frisbees

Price ($ per Frisbee)	Quantity Supplied (millions of Frisbees)
$2.00	50
$3.00	100
$4.00	150
$5.00	200

Plot the new supply schedule (on Plotting Demand for and Supply of Frisbees) and label it S_1. Label the new equilibrium E_1. Under these conditions, competitive market forces would tend to establish an equilibrium price of $__________ per Frisbee and an equilibrium quantity of __________ million Frisbees. Compared to the equilibrium price in question A, we say that, because of this change in *(price/underlying conditions)*, the *(supply/quantity supplied)* changed, and both the equilibrium price and the equilibrium quantity changed. The equilibrium price *(increased/decreased)* and the equilibrium quantity *(increased/decreased)*.

G. Now with the supply schedule at S_1, suppose further that a sharp drop in people's incomes as the result of a nationwide recession causes the demand schedule to change to the following:

Change in Demand for Frisbees

Price ($ per Frisbee)	Quantity Demanded (millions of Frisbees)
$1.00	200
$2.00	150
$3.00	100
$4.00	50

Plot the new demand schedule (on Plotting Demand for and Supply of Frisbees) and label it D_1. Label the new equilibrium E_2. Under these conditions, with the supply schedule at S_1, competitive market forces would tend to establish an equilibrium price of $__________ per Frisbee and an equilibrium quantity of __________ million Frisbees. Compared to the equilibrium price in question F, because of this change in *(price/underlying conditions)*, the *(demand/quantity demanded)* changed. The equilibrium price *(increased/decreased)* and the equilibrium quantity *(increased/decreased)*.

Unit 2, Lesson 11

Activity 1

Do Prices Matter to Consumers?

Part 1: The Consumers

Directions: As a group, predict the choices the following four people will make in the marketplace. Each has $100 to spend on items listed in the catalog attached to the end of this activity sheet. The total of the expenditures made for each person may come to less than $100, but it should fall somewhere between $90 and $100.

Jessica Jones

J.J., 17 years old, is enrolled in grade 11. She has just moved into the neighborhood and will start school tomorrow. She is a good student, likes to read, and is concerned about making new friends.

Jessica's Shopping List

	Item	Price
1.		
2.		
3.		
4.		
5.		
6.		

Harvey Hammer

H.H. is a 27-year-old carpenter. He is married, and he and his wife are expecting their second child. H.H. was told today that he has received a promotion and is now the foreman of a carpentry crew specializing in rough carpentry on home exteriors. In the past, Harvey was an inside finish carpenter.

Harvey's Shopping List

	Item	Price
1.		
2.		
3.		
4.		
5.		
6.		

Professor Willie Washington

W.W. is a 67-year-old university professor nearing the end of a successful career. She lives in a small apartment — alone except for her cat, Matilda. She spends most of her evening hours reading and grading papers.

Professor Washington's Shopping List

	Item	Price
1.		
2.		
3.		
4.		
5.		
6.		

Richie Mann

R.M. is an entrepreneur who is unmarried. While Richie is only 30 years old, he has already earned a great deal of money. He lives very well. He has cash accounts of more than $1 million, and he pays cash for what he buys. He also owns well over $1 million in stocks and bonds. Richie enjoys looking the part of a successful person.

Richie's Shopping List

	Item	Price
1.		
2.		
3.		
4.		
5.		
6.		

continued on next page  

Unit 2, Lesson 11

Activity 1

Part 2: Catalog of Possible Purchases

Item	Price
Designer jeans	$46.00
Current paperback novel	9.00
16-oz. hammer	12.00
Name-brand sweater	38.50
Dishwasher soap	2.50
Men's long underwear	13.50
Spiral notebook	1.00
Newspaper	.50
Steel-toe insulated boots	39.50
Brand X sweater	12.50
Light bulbs	2.00
Men's dress shirt	18.00
Sale-priced jeans	9.00
Reading lamp	19.00
Breath mints	2.00
Dress driving gloves	17.50
Lipstick	2.50
Men's dress socks	3.50
Dark suit	195.00
Box of chocolates	5.50

Item	Price
Pen	$2.50
Soup	.75/can
20-oz. framing hammer	22.00
Silk necktie	34.00
Rubber boots	18.50
Pencils (six)	1.50
Trapper-keeper with paper	8.50
Wine	9.00
Cat food	.50/can
Tape measure-50 ft.	14.00
Steaks (two)	9.00
Necktie	4.50
Chewing gum	1.00
Gold-plate pen	42.00
Work gloves	10.00
Cat caddy	38.50
Shampoo	1.50
Subscription to *Entrepreneur*	18.50
Signed picture, framed	75.00
Popular CD, Mad Monkeys	14.00

Unit 2, Lesson 12

Activity 1

Picturing and Calculating Elasticity

Pictures of market demand:

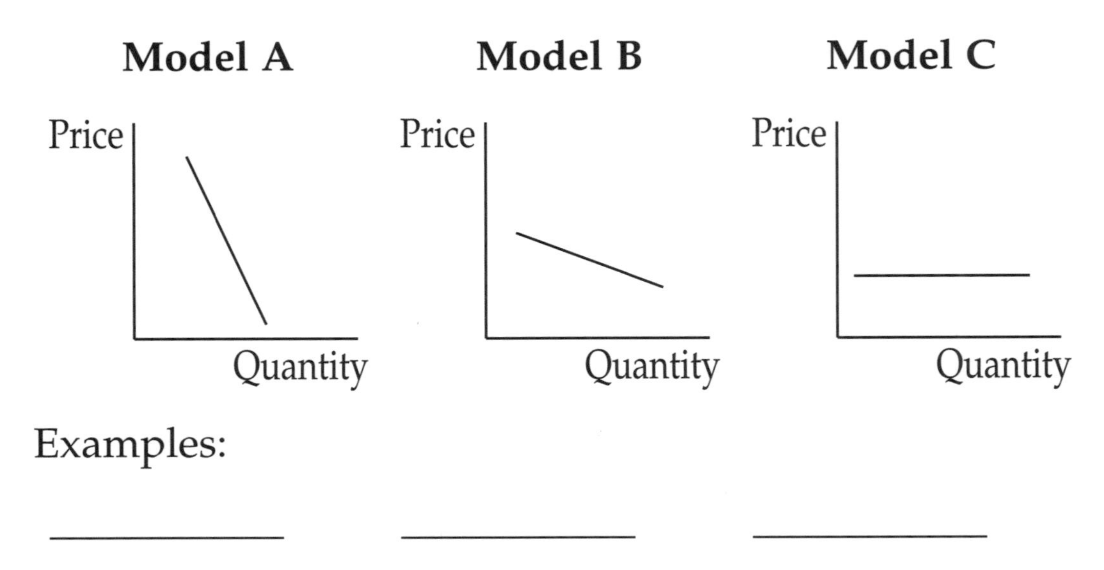

Examples:

____________ ____________ ____________

Using the following formula, calculate the price elasticity of demand for each product.

$$\text{Price elasticity of demand} = \frac{(Q2-Q1)/[(Q1+Q2)/2]}{(P2-P1)/[(P1+P2)/2]}$$

Price elasticity of demand for insulin:__________

Price elasticity of demand for a brand of orange juice:__________

Unit 2, Lesson 13

Activity 1

I, Pencil
by Leonard Read

I am a lead pencil — the ordinary wooden pencil familiar to all boys and girls and adults who can read and write.

Writing is both my vocation and my avocation; that's all I do.

You may wonder why I should write a genealogy. Well, to begin with, my story is interesting. And, next, I am a mystery — more so than a tree or a sunset or even a flash of lightning. But, sadly, I am taken for granted by those who use me, as if I were a mere incident and without background. This supercilious attitude relegates me to the level of the commonplace. This is a species of the grievous error in which mankind cannot too long persist without peril. For, the wise G.K. Chesterton observed, "We are perishing for want of wonder, not for want of wonders."

I, Pencil, simple though I appear to be, merit your wonder and awe, a claim I shall attempt to prove. In fact, if you can understand me — no, that's too much to ask of anyone — if you can become aware of the miraculousness which I symbolize, you can help save the freedom mankind is so unhappily losing. I have a profound lesson to teach. And I can teach this lesson better than can an automobile or an airplane or a mechanical dishwasher because — well, because I am seemingly so simple.

Simple? Yet *not a single person on the face of this earth knows how to make me.* This sounds fantastic, doesn't it? Especially when it is realized that there are about one and one-half billion of my kind produced in the U.S.A. each year.

Pick me up and look me over. What do you see? Not much meets the eye — there's some wood, lacquer, the printed labeling, graphite lead, a bit of metal, and an eraser.

INNUMERABLE ANTECEDENTS

Just as you cannot trace your family tree back very far, so is it impossible for me to name and explain all my antecedents. But I would like to suggest enough of them to impress upon you the richness and complexity of my background.

My family tree begins with what in fact is a tree, a cedar of straight grain that grows in Northern California and Oregon. Now contemplate all the saws and trucks and rope and the countless other gear used in harvesting and carting the cedar logs to the railroad siding. Think of all the persons and the numberless skills that went into their fabrication: the mining of ore, the making of steel and its refinement into saws, axes, motors; the growing of hemp and bringing it through all the stages to heavy and strong rope; the logging camps with their beds and mess halls, the cookery and the raising of all the foods. Why, untold thousands of persons had a hand in every cup of coffee the loggers drink!

The logs are shipped to a mill in San Leandro, California. Can you imagine the individuals who make flat cars and rails and railroad engines and who construct and install the communication systems incidental thereto? These legions are among my antecedents.

Consider the millwork in San Leandro. The cedar logs are cut into small, pencil-length slats less than one-fourth of an inch in thickness. These are kiln dried and then tinted for the same reason women put rouge on their faces. People prefer that I look pretty, not a pallid white. The slats are waxed and kiln dried again. How many skills went into the making of the tint and the kilns, into supplying the heat, the light and power, the belts, motors, and all the other things a mill requires? Sweepers in the mill among my ancestors? Yes, and included are the men who poured the concrete for the dam of a Pacific Gas & Electric Company hydroplant, which supplies the mill's power!

Don't overlook the ancestors present and distant who have a hand in transporting sixty carloads of slats across the nation.

Once in the pencil factory — $4,000,000 in machinery and buildings, all capital accumulated by thrifty and saving parents of mine — each slat is given eight grooves by a complex machine, after which another machine lays lead in every other slat, applies glue, and places another slat atop — a lead sandwich, so to speak. Seven brothers and I are mechanically carved from this "wood-clinched" sandwich.

My "lead" itself — it contains no lead at all — is complex. The graphite is mined in Ceylon. Consider these miners and those who make their many tools and the makers of the paper sacks in which the graphite is shipped and those who make the string that ties the sacks and those who put them aboard ships and those who make the ships. Even the lighthouse keepers along the way assisted in my birth — and the harbor pilots.

The graphite is mixed with clay from Mississippi in which ammonium hydroxide is used in the refining

Leonard Read, *I, Pencil,* originally published in *The Freeman,* December 1958.

continued on next page   

process. Then wetting agents are added, such as sulfonated tallow — animal fats chemically reacted with sulfuric acid. After passing through numerous machines, the mixture finally appears as endless extrusions — as from a sausage grinder — cut to size, dried, and baked for several hours at 1,850 degrees Fahrenheit. To increase their strength and smoothness the leads are then treated with a hot mixture which includes candelilla wax from Mexico, paraffin wax, and hydrogenated natural fats.

My cedar receives six coats of lacquer. Do you know all the ingredients of lacquer? Who would think that the growers of castor beans and the refiners of castor oil are a part of it? They are. Why, even the processes by which the lacquer is made a beautiful yellow involve the skills of more persons than one can enumerate!

Observe the labeling. That's a film formed by applying heat to carbon black mixed with resins. How do you make resins and what, pray, is carbon black?

My bit of metal — the ferrule — is brass. Think of all the persons who mine zinc and copper and those who have the skills to make shiny sheet brass from these products of nature. Those black rings on my ferrule are black nickel. What is black nickel and how is it applied? The complete story of why the center of my ferrule has no black on it would take pages to explain.

Then there's my crowning glory, inelegantly referred to in the trade as "the plug," the part man uses to erase the errors he makes with me. An ingredient called "factice" is what does the erasing. It is a rubber-like product made by reacting rapeseed oil from the Dutch East Indies with sulfur chloride. Rubber, contrary to the common notion, is only for binding purposes. Then, too, there are numerous vulcanizing and accelerating agents. The pumice comes from Italy; and the pigment which gives "the plug" its color is cadmium sulfide.

NO ONE KNOWS

Does anyone wish to challenge my earlier assertion that no single person on the face of this earth knows how to make me?

Actually, millions of human beings have had a hand in my creation, no one of whom even knows more than a very few of the others. Now, you may say that I go too far in relating the picker of a coffee berry in far off Brazil and food growers elsewhere to my creation; that this is an extreme position. I shall stand by my claim. There isn't a single person in all these millions, including the president of the pencil company, who contributes more than a tiny, infinitesimal bit of know-how. From the standpoint of know-how the only difference between the miner of graphite in Ceylon and the logger in Oregon is in the type of know-how. Neither the miner nor the logger can be dispensed with, any more than can the chemist at the factory or the worker in the oil field — paraffin being a by-product of petroleum.

Here is an astounding fact: Neither the worker in the oil field nor the chemist nor the digger of graphite or clay nor any who mans or makes the ships or trains or trucks nor the one who runs the machine that does the knurling on my bit of metal nor the president of the company performs his singular task because he wants me. Each one wants me less, perhaps, than does a child in the first grade. Indeed, there are some among this vast multitude who never saw a pencil, nor would they know how to use one. Their motivation is other than me. Perhaps it is something like this: Each of these millions sees that he can thus exchange his tiny know-how for the goods and services he needs or wants. I may or may not be among these items.

NO MASTER MIND

There is a fact still more astounding: The absence of a master mind, of anyone dictating or forcibly directing these countless actions which brings me into being. No trace of such a person can be found. Instead, we find the Invisible Hand at work. This is the mystery to which I earlier referred.

It has been said that "only God can make a tree." Why do we agree with this? Isn't it because we realize that we ourselves could not make one? Indeed, can we even describe a tree? We cannot, except in superficial terms. We can say, for instance, that a certain molecular configuration manifests itself as a tree. But what mind is there among men that could even record, let alone direct, the constant changes in molecules that transpire in the life span of a tree? Such a feat is utterly unthinkable!

I, Pencil, am a complex combination of miracles: a tree, zinc, copper, graphite, and so on. But to these miracles which manifest themselves in Nature an even more extraordinary miracle has been added: The configuration of creative human energies — millions of tiny know-hows configurating naturally and spontaneously in response to human necessity and desire and *in the absence of any human master-minding!* Since only God can make a tree, I insist that only God could make me. Man can no more direct these millions of know-hows to bring me into being than he can put molecules together to create a tree.

The above is what I meant when writing, "If you can become aware of the miraculousness which I symbolize, you can help save the freedom mankind is so unhappily losing." For, if one is aware that these know-hows will naturally, yet, automatically, arrange themselves into creative and productive patterns in response to human

continued on next page   

necessity and demand — that is, in the absence of governmental or any other coercive master-minding — then one will possess an absolutely essential ingredient for freedom: *A faith in free people.* Freedom is impossible without this faith.

Once government has had a monopoly of creative activity such as, for instance, the delivery of the mails, most individuals will believe that the mails could not be efficiently delivered by men acting freely. And here is the reason: Each one acknowledges that he himself doesn't know how to do all the things incident to mail delivery. He also recognizes that no other individual could do it. These assumptions are correct. No individual possesses enough know-how to perform a nation's mail delivery any more than any individual possesses enough know-how to make a pencil. No, in the absence of faith in free people — in the unawareness that millions of tiny know-hows would naturally and miraculously form and cooperate to satisfy this necessity — the individual cannot help but reach the erroneous conclusion that mail can be delivered only by governmental "master-minding."

Testimony Galore

If I, Pencil, were the only item that could offer testimony on what men and women can accomplish when free to try, then those with little faith would have a fair case. However, there is testimony galore; it's all about us and on every hand. Mail delivery is exceedingly simple when compared, for instance, to the making of an automobile or a calculating machine or a grain combine or a milling machine or to tens of thousands of other things. Delivery? Why, in this area where men have been left free to try, they deliver the human voice around the world in less than one second; they deliver an event visually and in motion to any person's home when it is happening; they deliver 150 passengers from Seattle to Baltimore in less than four hours; they deliver gas from Texas to one's range or furnace in New York at unbelievably low rates and without subsidy; they deliver four pounds of oil from the Persian Gulf to our Eastern Seaboard — halfway around the world — for less money than the government charges for delivering a one-ounce letter across the street!

The lesson I have to teach is this: *Leave all creative energies uninhibited.* Merely organize society to act in harmony with this lesson. Let society's legal apparatus remove all obstacles the best it can. Permit these creative know-hows freely to flow. Have faith that free men and women will respond to the Invisible Hand. This faith will be confirmed. I, Pencil, seemingly simple though I am, offer the miracle of my creation as testimony that this is a practical faith, as practical as the sun, the rain, a cedar tree, the good earth.

Questions for Discussion

A. How many people does it take to make a simple pencil?

____

____

____

B. Why would all these people cooperate in making a pencil?

____

____

____

C. What or who organizes all these people to make a pencil?

____

____

____

D. What is meant by the "invisible hand of the marketplace"?

____

____

____

E. Is it easier and more efficient for a pencil to be made by voluntary exchanges in the marketplace or by government rules?

____

____

____

F. What role do prices play in the making of a pencil?

____

____

____

Unit 2, Lesson 13

Activity 2

How Markets Allocate Resources

A market price, which is determined by supply and demand, is the mechanism that organizes an economy. These prices emerge from voluntary transactions among buyers and sellers. The order of a market economy is the result of millions of people seeking to further their own interests.

This means a change in the underlying conditions of one good not only changes the price of that good but the prices of thousands of other goods and services and the wages of people who produce them. Because of the prices, market economies allocate resources in the best interest of consumers.

Governments sometimes interfere in this process through regulations and price controls. The government policy usually is meant to solve an immediate "crisis," but the policy can cause unintended consequences that no one anticipated.

The following questions refer to a group of related markets during a long period of time. Assume that the markets are perfectly competitive and that the supply-and-demand model is completely applicable. The diagrams show the supply and demand in each market *before* the assumed change occurs. Trace through the effects of the assumed change, *other things constant.* Work your way from left to right. Shift only one curve in each market.

For each market, draw whatever new supply or demand curve is needed, labeling each new curve S_1 or D_1. Then circle the correct symbol under each diagram (⇑ for increase, - for unchanged, and ⇓ for decrease). Remember to shift only one curve in each market.

1. Improvements in technology reduce the cost of producing DVD players.

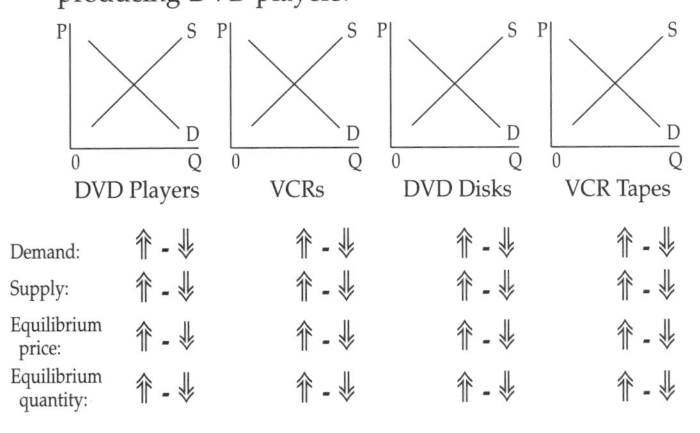

2. Assume that a heavy frost destroys half the world's coffee crop, and that people use more cream in their coffee than they do in tea.

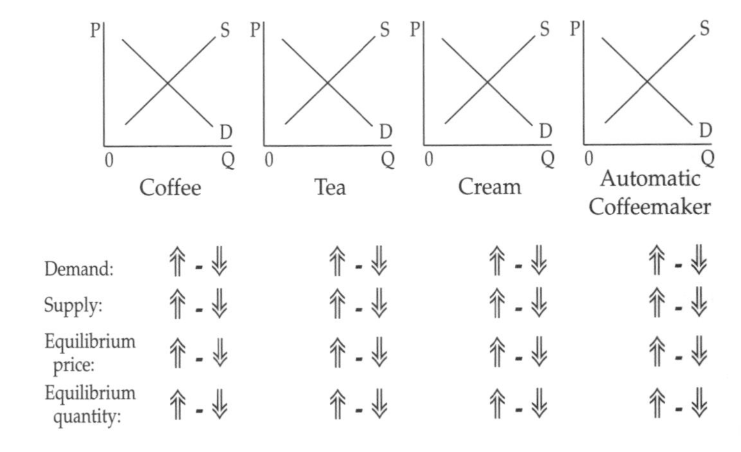

3. Assume that environmental regulations and people's concerns about building power plants near their homes reduce the number of power plants built in California.

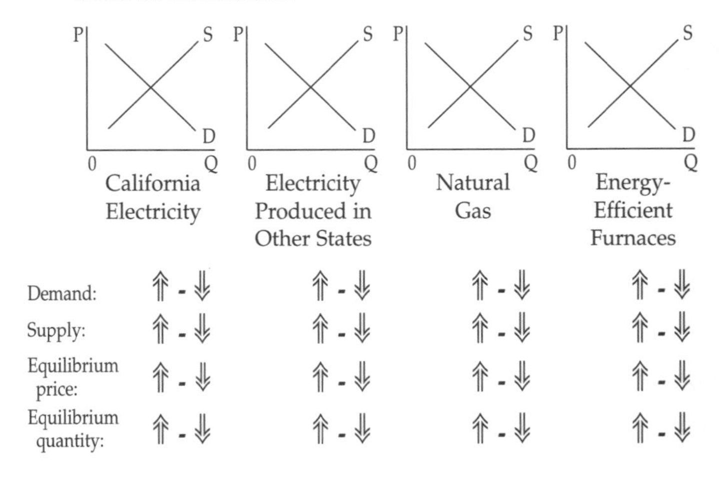

4. Assume that soccer becomes the national pastime, and attendance at professional soccer games exceeds attendance at professional baseball games.

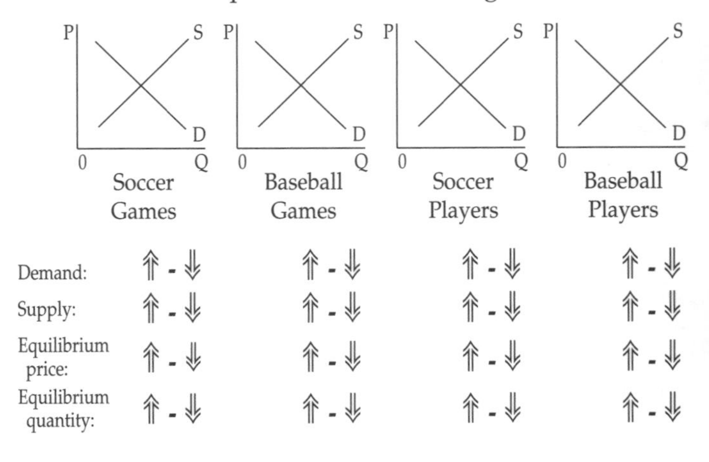

continued on next page  

5. Assume that there is a new federal law that places a 200 percent excise tax on the sale of yachts.

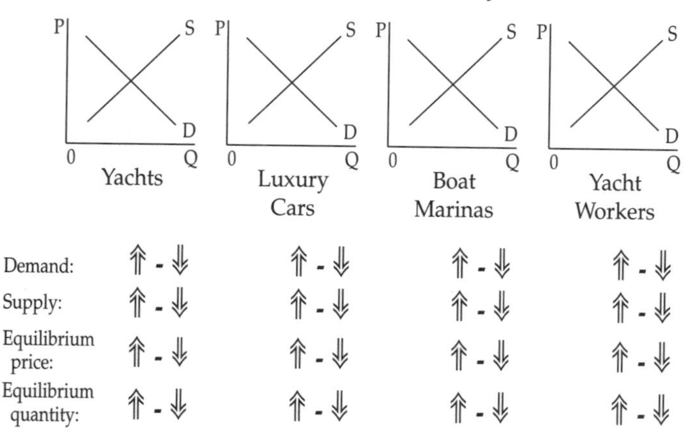

6. Assume that the government imposes a tariff or tax on foreign steel to save the jobs of American steel-workers. Steel is a major component of automobiles.

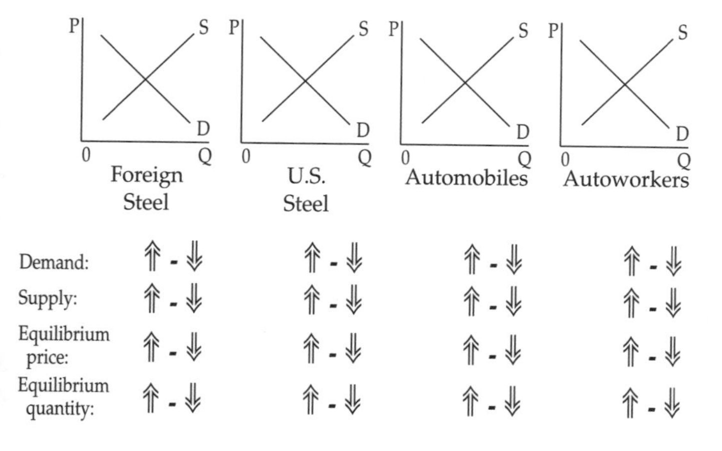

Unit 2, Lesson 14

Activity 1

What Will Happen If?

Directions: Read the following descriptions and decide if there will be surplus or a shortage of the product in each situation. Check the correct answer.

A. A very popular singer is coming to a town to perform a concert in a concert hall that seats 10,000 people. The ticket price for the concert is $30.00 per person. There are 30,000 fans in the area who are willing to pay $80.00 per seat to listen to the concert. What will happen?

Shortage of seats ___________ Surplus of seats ___________

B. A very popular singer is coming to town to perform a concert in a concert hall that seats 10,000 people. The ticket price for the concert is $30,000 per person. There are 3,000 fans in the area who are willing to pay $80.00 to listen to the concert. What will happen?

Shortage of seats ___________ Surplus of seats ___________

C. The Ford Motor Company has designed a new car that resembles a Ford model that was popular 40 years ago. Ford plans to produce 100,000 of the new-old cars each year. Ford will price these cars at $24,000 and require dealers not to change that price. There are 200,000 people per year who wish to buy the car. What will happen?

Shortage of seats ___________ Surplus of seats ___________

D. The Fish and Wildlife Department in a West Coast state decides to allow people to dig for razor clams on the ocean beaches three days each year. There is a small charge ($10) for a license to dig these clams. Millions of people enjoy eating razor clams. During most of the year they buy razor clams in fishmarkets for $20 to $30 a dozen. What will happen on the days when people can dig razor clams for themselves?

Shortage of seats ___________ Surplus of seats ___________

E. Schools ask students to take good care of their textbooks during the year and to return them on the last day of school. Often students turn back the books in poor condition. In an effort to encourage students to take better care of the books, the School Board offers to pay students $2,000 for any textbook returned in good condition. What will happen?

Shortage of seats ___________ Surplus of seats ___________

UNIT 3

HOW YOU CAN PROSPER IN A MARKET ECONOMY

Lesson 15

Activity 1 Why Do Some People Earn More than Others?

Lesson 16

Activity 1 Making Choices about Saving and Investing

Lesson 17

Activity 1 Financial Planning Document

Lesson 18

Activity 1 Buying on Credit

Lesson 19

Activity 1 What Will People Be Doing in 2010?

Activity 2 Who Are the Entrepreneurs?

Unit 3, Lesson 15

Activity 1

Why Do Some People Earn More Than Others?

The mystery in this case has to do with why some people earn more than others. In a market economy like the United States, we have a wide variation in incomes for people in various occupations. What explains these wide differences?

Recall the **Guide to Economic Reasoning**:

1. People choose.
2. People's choices involve costs.
3. People respond to incentives in predictable ways.
4. People create economic systems that influence individual choices and incentives.
5. People gain when they trade voluntarily.
6. People's choices have consequences that lie in the future.

Now, let's examine the answers to the True-False questions.

A. People with more formal education earn less on average than people with less formal education.

The answer is *false*. Gary Becker, recipient of the 1992 Nobel Memorial Prize in Economics Science, has explained that gaining a high school and college education raises a person's income even after accounting for the direct costs (e.g., tuition and books) and the indirect costs (e.g., income that a person could otherwise have earned during the time he or she spent in school) of getting that education. High school and college education raise a person's income regardless of intelligence or family wealth. This is not a shock. People in all generations have known that having a good education on average results in a better income. Current evidence is provided by U.S. Census Bureau data. Examine the following table to look for the relationship between level of formal education and median income.

Level of Educational Attainment and Income

Source: U.S. Census Bureau, 2000

Level of Education	Median Income of Both Sexes, Aged 25 Years and Older
Not a High School Graduate	$11,606
High School Graduate (Includes GED)	$19,979
Some College, No Degree	$25,498
Associate's Degree	$27,493
Bachelor's Degree	$36,715
Master's Degree	$47,468
Professional Degree	$67,462

B. The laws of demand and supply do not apply to wages and salaries.

The answer is *false*. The laws of demand and supply do apply to markets for various jobs. The wage or salary paid to a worker is a reflection of the market price for labor. It reflects how much businesses are willing and able to offer. It also reflects how much workers are willing to accept.

Labor markets, like many other markets, are often changing. A change in demand or supply for an occupation results in a shift in the demand curve or the supply curve for that occupation. For example, demand for software engineers is likely to increase faster than the demand for most other workers. Demand for machinists is likely to decrease more than the demand for most other workers. Similarly, the supply of workers influences the market price of labor. The supply of carpenters is likely to decrease because many potential workers prefer more comfortable working conditions. This will result in a shift in supply for carpenters.

What about celebrities and professional athletes? While the demand is high for superstars, the supply is low. Superstars are able to deliver their services to millions of fans by way of television, movies, and other media. Thus, the equilibrium price of their labor is likely to be at a high level.

Even given the high salaries they often earn, however, celebrities and superstars might actually look like bargains to their employers. If this seems surprising, consider that markets for celebrities are similar to Wal-Mart or other firms that sell in large

continued on next page   

volume at low cost. Technology (television, the Internet, CDs, and so forth) now enables consumers to buy the services of their favorite entertainers at a relatively low cost. Turn on the Today Show and you (and millions of others) can watch Katie Couric. Go to the Internet and you (and millions of others) can download the music of your favorite artist. Easy access to sports and entertainment via the media means high-volume sales for advertisers and others who benefit, for example, from various licensing arrangements. High-volume sales produce high levels of revenue. The income celebrities receive — compared to the revenue they generate for the entertainment industry — may actually be low.

C. Natural ability and willingness to work hard contribute little to earning more income.

The answer is *false*. Natural abilities such as strength, good looks, coordination, and intelligence are all factors that have some bearing on income. They obviously are important in the market for celebrities. Celebrities are often very attractive or possessed of remarkable skills (few among us can throw a 90-miles-per-hour fast ball, hitting the outside corner of the plate, low, nine times out of ten). And apart from uncommon abilities, some people are more willing than others to work hard. Employers reward workers for how well they produce. Those who work hard are more likely to produce well than those who do not. All of these characteristics tend to be reflected in the market price for labor.

QUESTIONS FOR DISCUSSION

A. Describe the relationship between level of education and median income.

____

____

____

B. In 2000, how much more would a college graduate have earned per year than a high school graduate?

____

C. Assuming a 40-year work life and no pay increases along the way, how much more might a college graduate expect to earn than a high school graduate?

____

D. Solve the mystery: Why is it that people in diverse occupations, occupations that contribute in very different ways to the social good, earn such different incomes?

____

____

____

____

____

____

E. Why do celebrities seem to earn so much income?

____

____

____

Unit 3, Lesson 16

Activity 1

Making Choices about Saving and Investing

Part 1: Saving and Inflation

Your friend Jackie is thinking about buying a used car for $3,500. It looks like a nice car — dependable and safe. Jackie is very close to her Aunt Jennifer. Aunt Jennifer checked with Jackie's mother and learned that Jackie had already saved $500 toward buying the used car.

Aunt Jennifer decided to give Jackie a surprise birthday gift of $3,000. Jackie now has enough money to buy the car!

Still, Jackie has a new problem. She sees two choices. First, she could save the $3,500 and wait one year to buy the car. After all, before she received the gift from Aunt Jennifer, she thought it would take her a year or two to save enough to buy the car. Jackie knows that she could earn 3 percent interest per year if she were to place the $3,500 in a savings account. Maybe she could use the interest to buy a cool pair of sunglasses and driving gloves. Jackie also knows that the expected change in overall prices for next year, including prices for used cars, is similar to this year's price increase, a 5 percent number. Second, Jackie could buy the used car now.

What should she do? Let's check the math.

- How much would Jackie have in her account if she saved the $3,500 for one year? Fill in the blanks to show your answers.

  Savings account

Deposit	$3,500.00
Add interest earned ($3,500 x .03)	_______
Total	_______

- How much would the car cost Jackie if she waited a year to buy it? Fill in the blanks to show your answers.

  Price of the used car

Price	$3,500.00
Add inflation ($3,500 x .05)	_______
New price at year's end	_______

- What do you think Jackie should do?

  ____

  ____

  ____

Part 2: Compounding Interest and the Rule of 72

Thanks in part to Aunt Jennifer, Jackie now has $3,500. She has checked with Aunt Jennifer, and Aunt Jennifer agrees that if Jackie would prefer not to buy a car now, it would be fine to use the money in another way.

Jackie has learned that savings can grow over time, and that the growth in earnings can be surprising. Here is how it works. Suppose Jackie put $1,000 into an account that pays 10 percent interest and left it there for 10 years. You might expect that Jackie would have earnings of $1,000 — or a total of $2,000 — at the end of the 10 years ($1,000 x 10 percent x 10 years = $1,000). You would be wrong. Jackie would have more than that. How? The return would be higher because Jackie would not only earn interest on the principal (the original $1,000), she would also earn interest on the interest paid annually. This is called *compounding*.

Here is how compounding works. Let's assume that Jackie can earn 10 percent interest, compounded annually.

- At the end of year 1, Jackie will have earned $100 in interest. Then she will have $1,100 in her account ($1,000 principal + $100 interest).
- At the end of year 2, Jackie will have a total value of $1,210 ($1,000 in principal + $100 interest from year 1 + $110 interest from year 2).
- At the end of year 3, Jackie will have a total value of $1,331 ($1,000 in principal + $100 interest from year 1 + $110 interest from year 2 + $121 interest from year 3).
- And so forth for 10 years. At the end of 10 years, Jackie's $1,000 will have grown to $2,852.67.

The Rule of 72 can help Jackie calculate the benefit she can gain by saving. The Rule of 72 tells how many years it will take for savings to double at a certain interest rate, as long as the saver doesn't withdraw the earnings. To use the Rule of 72, divide 72 by the real interest rate.

Jackie is considering four ways of investing her $3,500, as shown below. Use the Rule of 72 to calculate how many years will it take her to double her money in each of the four cases.

Form of savings	Real interest or rate of return	Years to double
Passbook savings	2%	
Money market account	5%	
U.S. Treasury Bond	6%	
Stock market	10%	

continued on next page   

Part 3: Jackie Is One of Many: The Loanable Funds Market

Jackie will make her decision regarding the $3,500 according to what she thinks is in her own interest. However, Jackie's decision, together with the decisions of many other savers, can have widespread implications, influencing the economy generally. If Jackie does choose to save her money, she will also be adding money to the loanable funds market. The loanable funds market is the money available for borrowing and lending. Imagine that Jackie decides to deposit her $3,500 in a bank account. Banks and other financial institutions use money deposited by savers like Jackie to make loans to individuals and businesses. Thus a business person might borrow Jackie's money and use it, for example, to expand a company, thus increasing the productive potential of the economy.

By adding money into the loanable funds market, Jackie and others who save reduce the price of money because — everything else held constant — an increased supply of savings dollars shifts the supply curve for dollars to the right, causing the price of money (the interest rate) to fall. When people fail to save, they reduce the supply of savings dollars and shift the supply curve for dollars to the left, causing the price of money (the interest rate) to increase.

QUESTIONS FOR DISCUSSION

A. What is the loanable funds market?

____

____

____

B. How does increasing savings cause interest rates to decrease?

____

____

____

C. How does reducing savings cause interest rates to increase?

____

____

____

Unit 3, Lesson 17

Activity 1

Financial Planning Document

Name of planner ______________________________

Date ________________

Part 1: Goal Statements

List short-term goals:

____
____
____
____
____

List medium-term goals:

____
____
____
____
____

List long-term goals:

____
____
____
____
____

Part 2: Income Information

Complete the following, using monthly figures:

Sources of income	Amount of income
Wages	________
Gifts	________
Allowance	________
Interest on savings	________
Sales	________
Other	________
Total	$________

Part 3: Expenditures

Complete the following, using monthly figures:

Expenditures	Amount of expenditure
Housing	________
Food	________
Clothing	________
School supplies	________
Job equipment	________
Car payment	________
Gas and oil	________
Car maintenance	________
Car insurance	________
Medical care	________
Entertainment	________
Taxes	________
Personal care	________
Gifts	________
Savings	________
Credit cards	________
Other	________
Total	$________

continued on next page

Part 4: What Do the Numbers Tell You?

Calculate your discretionary income by subtracting your total monthly expenses from your total monthly income.

Total monthly income: $________________

Total monthly expenses: $________________

Discretionary income: $________________

Given your monthly income, monthly expenses, and discretionary income, evaluate your ability to attain the goals and live the lifestyle you have selected. Are your short-, medium-, and/or long-term goals being met? Will you be able to meet them in the future, given your financial condition and plan? Write your evaluative statement below.

____

____

____

____

____

____

____

____

____

____

Unit 3, Lesson 18

Activity 1

Buying on Credit

A world of scarcity forces people to choose among competing alternatives. Naturally, people try to pick the alternative that provides the greatest expected benefit at the lowest expected cost. Sometimes alternatives have such high costs that they are quickly rejected.

Because the calculation of benefits and costs focuses on expected, future consequences, it is difficult to identify all of them accurately. This makes it important to do the best we can and to use what we know about costs and benefits. Consumers often fail to do this.

Directions: Read each of the three cases that follow. Review the stated alternatives each person has identified and determine the expected costs and benefits for each. After reviewing your cost and benefit calculations, make a recommendation as to what the person in each case should do.

Case One

For her 18th birthday, Katie Jackson has received gifts of cash totaling $75. All the birthday cards that had money in them said, in effect, "Go out and buy something you'd really like to have." Katie wants to do just that. At her favorite department store, Katie eyes a leather skirt. "It is perfect," she says as she looks for the price tag. The tag shows that the price is $275. But wait a minute: it is on sale for 50 percent off! "That is a sizeable discount," says a voice from behind the blouse rack. A salesperson is speaking; she continues: "And besides that, if you open a credit-card account at our store now, you will get 10 percent more off all of your purchases here today." Katie wonders what her best choice is. She knows that she has $500 in her college-fund savings account, and she could use money from this account to cover the cost of the skirt.

A quick review of the store's credit application reveals a 21 percent interest rate charged on unpaid balances, a 30-day grace period, and a late fee of $35.

What are the alternatives for Katie? What are the costs and benefits of each alternative? What should she do?

Alternatives for Katie

- Don't buy, seek a cheaper skirt.

  Costs ______________________________

  ____

  Benefits ______________________________

  ____

- Buy, but don't apply for a credit card; use savings to pay for the balance.

  Costs ______________________________

  ____

  Benefits ______________________________

  ____

- Buy and apply for the credit card, using credit for the purchase.

  Costs ______________________________

  ____

  Benefits ______________________________

  ____

- Buy on credit and pay $75 on the balance, carrying over the rest.

  Costs ______________________________

  ____

  Benefits ______________________________

  ____

- Buy on credit and pay the balance when the bill arrives, using the birthday money and savings.

  Costs ______________________________

  ____

  Benefits ______________________________

  ____

What decision do you recommend for Katie? Explain briefly.

____

____

____

continued on next page  

Case Two

In two months Willie Wheels will graduate from the University of South Dakota with a Business Administration degree. He knows that as soon as he gets a real job his first big purchase will be a new car. He is not sure what brand or model he will buy, but he believes the new car will cost him about $25,000. Willie has no money left in his savings account, and he owes $15,000 on his school loans.

Although Willie has not landed a job yet, he has had some good interviews, and his buddies (all with lower grade-point averages) have gotten jobs paying about $26,000 per year to start. Just for fun, Willie stops by the local Honda dealer and sees the car of his dreams, with a CD player, moon roof, leather seats, a V-6 engine, spoiler, and aluminum wheels. A quick look at the window sticker puts Willie in sticker shock. The manufacturer's suggested price is $29,500. That includes set-up and delivery, but not the six percent sales tax and license fee of $150.

"You're in luck," says the car salesperson. "Honda has just put a $2,500 rebate on this model for in-stock inventory. And I see you're wearing a USD letter jacket. Will you graduate soon?" Without waiting for an answer, the salesperson continues: "I'll also discount the price by $500 for you as a first-time college-graduate buyer, and if you plan to graduate this spring that is close enough." Willie begins to think this purchase might be possible, but still he isn't sure. "I don't have any money for a down payment, and I won't be on the job for another two months," he says. "You're in luck, again," the friendly dealer explains; "this dealership has a no-money-down, payments-don't-start-for-90-days plan, and we can finance your loan at 3.9 percent for 48 months. If you need more time, we have an 8.9 interest rate for 60-month loans."

As Willie begins to consider the purchase, he remembers the need to determine the real interest rate in determining costs and benefits. His economics professor mentioned in class that the economy will most likely experience a five percent rate of inflation for the foreseeable future.

What are the alternatives for Willie? What are the costs and benefits of each alternative? What should Willie do?

Alternatives for Willie

- Turn tail and run!

  Costs ______________________________

  ____

  Benefits ______________________________

  ____

- Buy the car, using a 48-month loan.

  Costs ______________________________

  ____

  Benefits ______________________________

  ____

- Buy the car, using a 60-month loan.

  Costs ______________________________

  ____

  Benefits ______________________________

  ____

- Consider the cheaper model: no $2,500 rebate, but a base price of $19,850; all other incentives are the same.

  Costs ______________________________

  ____

  Benefits ______________________________

  ____

What decision do you recommend for Willie? Explain briefly.

____

____

____

continued on next page   

CASE THREE

Mr. and Mrs. Jones have taken the big step and purchased a new home. It is the fulfillment of their dreams: a modest two-story home in the suburbs. Mr. and Mrs. Jones are both employed; together they earn $45,000 per year. The down payment on the house has emptied their savings account. Unfortunately, they have just learned that their new house comes with all appliances except for a clothes washer and dryer. This fact somehow slipped through the cracks in their earlier negotiations over the house, and now buying a washer and dryer has become a top priority, especially because Mrs. Jones is expecting a child in three months.

As Mr. and Mrs. Jones drive home to their apartment — soon to be their former apartment, since they plan to move into their home this weekend — they see a huge SALE sign in the window of an appliance store. Mr. Jones steers the car into the parking lot. As they walk toward the store, he and Mrs. Jones both eye the "Visa Card Welcomed Here" sticker affixed to the door.

Sure enough, the showroom floor is stocked with a full array of washers, dryers, and washer-and-dryer combinations. Big ones, little ones, top loaders, front loaders, various colors, stainless steel models — wow! Because Mr. Jones usually does the laundry, he looks at all the combos carefully and identifies two he thinks will work. The first set has a smaller capacity, is white in color, and has a one-year parts-and-labor warranty; it costs $579. The second set has a larger capacity, comes with a stainless-steel tub and has a three-year parts-and-labor warranty. This combo is on sale for $849, and it also comes with a free, mail-in silver service set valued at $129. "You can't go wrong on either set at these prices," comments the salesperson. "Free delivery, and the company picks up the sales tax if you buy today." Mrs. Jones pulls Mr. Jones aside; they discuss the fact that they don't have cash for the purchase, and they are confident that if they applied for a secured loan the request would be denied because of the large debt they are already carrying with their home mortgage. "But we could use the new Visa card we just received in the mail," says Mr. Jones; "there is no balance on that card."

Mr. and Mrs. Jones must pay interest at a rate of 21 percent on unpaid credit-card balances. The minimum payment is five percent of the balance each month.

What are the alternatives for Mr. and Mrs. Jones? What are the costs and benefits for each alternative? What should they do?

Alternatives for Mr. and Mrs. Jones

- Don't buy, use the laundromat.

  Costs ______________________

  ____

  Benefits ______________________

  ____

- Buy the $579 combo and charge it on Visa

  Costs ______________________

  ____

  Benefits ______________________

  ____

- Buy the $849 combo, charge it on Visa, and be sure to send for the free silver service.

  Costs ______________________

  ____

  Benefits ______________________

  ____

What decision do you recommend for the Joneses? Explain briefly.

____

____

____

Unit 3, Lesson 19

Activity 1

What Will People Be Doing in 2010? Bureau of Labor Statistics 2000-2010 Employment Projections

Source: Internet: http://www.bls.gov/emp

The Bureau of Labor Statistics, U.S. Department of Labor, publishes projections for the American workforce. These projections provide information on where future job growth is expected. Growth projections are then categorized by industry sector, by occupation, and by the likely composition of the workforce pursuing those jobs.

The 10-year projections are widely used in career guidance, in the planning of education and training programs, and in studying long-range employment trends.

EMPLOYMENT GROWTH

Over the 2000-2010 period, total employment is projected to increase by 15 percent, slightly less than the 17 percent growth during the previous decade, 1990-2000.

SECTOR EMPLOYMENT

- The service-producing sector (including a broad range of occupation categories — from custodial services to medical and legal services, etc.) will continue to be the dominant generator of employment in the economy, adding 20.5 million jobs by 2010. Within the goods-producing sector, construction and durable manufacturing will contribute relatively modest employment gains.
- As employment in the service-producing sector increases by 19 percent, manufacturing employment is expected to increase by only 3 percent over the 2000-2010 period. Manufacturing will return to its 1990 employment level of 19.1 million, but its share of total jobs is expected to decline from 13 percent in 2000 to 11 percent in 2010.
- Health services, business services, social services, engineering, management, and related services are expected to account for almost one of every two nonfarm wage and salary jobs added to the economy during the 2000-2010 period. These sectors account for a large share of the fastest-growing industries.

OCCUPATIONAL EMPLOYMENT

- Professional and related occupations and service occupations are projected to increase the fastest and to add the most jobs: 7.0 million and 5.1 million, respectively. These two groups — on opposite ends of the educational attainment and earnings spectrum — are expected to provide more than half of total job growth over the 2000-2010 period.
- Transportation and material moving occupations are projected to grow by 15 percent, about the same as the average for all occupations.
- Office and administrative support occupations are projected to grow more slowly than average, reflecting long-term trends in office automation. Production occupations should grow much more slowly than average because of advances in manufacturing technology.
- Eight of the 10 fastest-growing occupations are computer-related, commonly referred to as information technology occupations.

EDUCATION AND TRAINING

- Employment in all education or training categories that generally require a college degree or other post secondary training will grow faster than the average rate across all occupations. These categories accounted for 29 percent of all jobs in 2000, but they will account for 42 percent of projected new job growth, 2000-2010.
- The four categories requiring work-related training are projected to grow more slowly than average, but they will still add a substantial number of jobs.

LABOR FORCE

- The civilian labor force is projected to increase by 17 million over the 2000-2010 period, reaching 158 million in 2010. This 12 percent increase is only slightly greater than the 11.9 percent increase over the previous decade, 1990-2000, when the labor force grew by 15 million. The demographic composition of the labor force is expected to change because of changes in the composition of the population and in the rates of workforce participation across demographic groups.
- In 2010, the baby-boom cohort will be aged 46 to 64, and this age group will account for a substantial share of the labor force. The median age of the labor force will continue to rise, even though the youth labor force (aged 16 to 24) is expected to grow more rapidly than the overall labor force for the first time in 25 years.
- Labor force participation rates of women in nearly all age groups are projected to increase. The women's labor force will grow more rapidly than the men's, and the women's share of the labor force will increase sharply from 47 percent in 2000 to 48 percent in 2010.

continued on next page   

- The labor force groups designated Asian and other and Hispanic are projected to increase faster than other groups (44 percent and 36 percent, respectively) because of high net immigration and higher than average fertility. The African American labor force is expected to grow by 21 percent, more than twice as fast as the 9 percent growth rate for the white labor force.
- The share of the labor force will increase from 5 to 6 percent for the Asian and other group and from 11 to 13 percent for Hispanics. White non-Hispanics accounted for 73 percent of the labor force in 2000. Their share of the labor force in 2010 will decrease to 69 percent.

QUESTIONS FOR DISCUSSION

A. Is the manufacturing or service sector likely to expand more?

____

____

____

B. What are some of the fastest-growing sectors?

____

____

____

C. What occupations are projected to grow more slowly?

____

____

____

D. How are education and training important?

____

____

____

E. How is the labor force likely to change?

____

____

____

Unit 3, Lesson 19

Activity 2

Who Are the Entrepreneurs?

Entrepreneurs are risk takers. They combine productive resources (natural resources, labor resources, and capital resources) in new ways to produce new goods and services. American history, more than that of any other nation, is marked by the achievements of entrepreneurs. They include, among many others, Cyrus McCormick and the reaper, Andrew Carnegie in steel, John D. Rockefeller in oil, and Henry Ford in automobiles.

Thanks to entrepreneurs, technological advances have transformed American life throughout the past two centuries. Try to imagine a world without automobiles, cell phones, television sets, computers, copy machines, the Internet, ballpoint pens, air conditioning, antibiotics, anesthetics, and so forth. It would indeed be a different world.

What are the characteristics of entrepreneurs? Read the following case studies and respond to the questions that follow.

Case Study 1

Entrepreneur: **Thanh Lam**

Company: **Ba-Le, Inc. & Dba Ba-Le Sandwich & Bakery**

Mr. Thanh Lam is a successful retailer of Vietnamese-style sandwiches, pastries, and noodle dishes; he is also a wholesaler of baked goods and deli sandwiches, selling to airlines, food caterers, hotels, supermarkets, and restaurants throughout Hawaii.

Mr. Lam arrived in the United States from a Malaysian refugee camp in 1979. He had little money and spoke little English. By December 1984, he opened the first Ba-Le sandwich shop. Soon Mr. Lam was also baking and selling his own bread. In 1996, Mr. Lam began offering catering services. By 1999, Mr. Lam's customers included the Hilton and Sheraton hotel chains and several airlines including Continental, Japan Airlines, Delta, American, United, China Airlines, and Air New Zealand. Mr. Lam also produces fresh pizza dough for Papa John's in Hawaii. His business now is expanding to Japan and China.

Case Study 2

Entrepreneur: **Joseph J. Atick**

Company: **Visionics**

Joseph J. Atick makes biometrics software that matches facial measurements against information in a database; the output of this matching can be used to identify individuals.

As security procedures become increasingly important in airports and other high-risk environments, Mr. Atick's products are proving to be very valuable as tools for identifying potential terrorists. They have many other uses as well--in helping law enforcement officers find runaways, for example.

Mr. Atick, a former physicist, invented the technology needed to manufacture these products. The demand for them appears to be increasing. The biometrics market is expected to quadruple by 2004.

Case Study 3

Entrepreneur: **Belinda Guadarrama**

Company: **GC Micro**

Belinda Guadarrama was working for a small mail-order business north of San Francisco when the company went out of business. She liked the area, and rather than move to a job elsewhere she decided to open her own business. In 1986, Ms. Guadarrama started GC Micro, with two employees. The firm, which began as a value-added reseller of software products, was financed by the sale of her home and some money from a retirement account.

Today GC Micro is a leading supplier of computer hardware and software products to the defense and aerospace industries. The company employs 28 workers and, in 2000, had sales of $34 million.

Ms. Guadarrama says that satisfying her customers is her first priority. She believes that, to be a success in business, you must be willing to invest your own money, develop a good five-year business plan and stick to it, work long days for a long time, and give your customers high levels of service and attention. Moreover, she believes customer satisfaction is related to how well her own employees enjoy their jobs. She suggests that successful business people should treat their employees like business partners.

continued on next page

QUESTIONS FOR DISCUSSION

A. What traits to do entrepreneurs like Mr. Lam, Mr. Atick, and Ms. Guadarrama seem to have in common?

B. How do entrepreneurs like Mr. Lam, Mr. Atick, and Ms. Guadarrama benefit our economy?

C. How do entrepreneurs help other people to earn income?

UNIT 4

THE BUSINESS OF DOING BUSINESS

Unit 4, Lesson 20

Activity 1

A Visit with Adam Smith

Adam Smith was an 18th-century philosopher who is highly regarded today for having explained many of the basic principles of market economies. Here are a few facts regarding Professor Smith.

- Adam Smith was born in Kirkcaldy, Scotland, in 1723.
- In 1751 Smith was appointed professor of logic and then professor of moral philosophy at Glasgow University in Scotland.
- In 1759, he published *Theory of Moral Sentiments,* a book that established his reputation as an intellectual leader. In this book Smith defines virtue and discusses why we should live a virtuous life.
- Smith spent 10 years writing his most well-known book, *An Inquiry Into the Nature and Causes of the Wealth of Nations* — usually referred to as *The Wealth of Nations.* Published in 1776, this book established Smith as the founder of modern economic thought. In it, he offers an extensive description of the principles of market economies.
- In 1777, Smith became Commissioner of Customs for Scotland.
- People who knew Smith often commented on his charm and intelligence; they also observed that Smith was the epitome of the absent-minded professor.

NASA Experiments with the ICCDSCU

NASA scientists have developed something called the Inter-Century Cross Dimensional Satellite Communication Unit (to make it easy: the ICCDSCU). It allows scholars from different time periods to communicate with one another. Today NASA is hosting a panel discussion attended by prominent economists and other thinkers. They will pose questions to Adam Smith, the founder of modern economic thought.

Panel Moderator Professor Smith, thank you so much for accepting our call. Welcome to the technology of the 21st century. We are delighted that you are willing to speak with us.

Professor Smith Thank you. I certainly don't understand how this conversation across time is possible. But I am happy to speak with you. By the way, I wonder if your amazing machine could tell me where I might have placed my eyeglasses? They always seem to be …hmmm, aaahhh…lost….

Panel Moderator I will tell my people to get in touch with your people so that we can arrange to scan your home and try to spot your glasses with our laser eyeglasses detectors. In the meantime, Professor Smith, here is your first question. It comes from one of your friends and countrymen — philosopher, historian, and economist David Hume.

Mr. Hume It is good to speak with you again, my friend, even under these extraordinary circumstances. Here is my question. I suspect that, even in the 21st century, people are still trying to understand the operation of market economies, the very topic you wrote about so well back in 1776. People persist in thinking that the men and women who run businesses in market economies are motivated by greed. It is all anyone talks about in the popular media. Greed, as you well know, Professor Smith, is associated with earning profits. And greed is not a positive character trait. It brings to mind all sorts of disagreeable connotations. What do you say to those who regard business people as greedy, selfish, money-grubbing dolts?

Professor Smith I once referred to England as a nation of shopkeepers. Perhaps you remember that. I meant that remark as a compliment to the people of England. The values of the merchant include honesty, trustworthiness, peace, and cooperation. These are positive values, not negative ones.

Mr. Hume Perhaps you are right. But you are avoiding my question. What about the negative trait of greed and its association with markets?

Professor Smith You always have been keen on maintaining a sharp focus, David. Very well then: The word *greed* does suggest unsavory, brutish behavior.

continued on next page   

Yet in some cases we admire greed. Greed may imply working competitively to achieve a goal, as in the case of scientists who are greedy in their search for new explanations or new medicines. Olympic athletes are greedy about setting new records. Poets are greedy for the satisfaction, and perhaps also the acclaim, they gain by writing new verse. All this seems unremarkable. Unfortunately, the same drive and determination that people admire in these cases tend to be less admired in businesspeople.

M. Voltaire Yes, of course. I have heard you say that many times. But for some reason we continue to regard greed as bad. Who would choose to sit at a sidewalk café with people who are greedy and selfish?

Professor Smith Ah, Monsieur Voltaire. How kind of you to join us. You ask pointed questions, as usual, and I know you are particular about the company you keep. But I fear that I have been misunderstood regarding this point about greed and selfishness. Let me put it this way. There is a difference between people who are selfish and people who are self-interested. While some people are selfish, all people act in their own self-interest. Self-interested behavior may be selfish, but it is not necessarily so.

Professor Hayek *Not necessarily so:* It is a view I should think the skeptical Frenchman would approve. I also have thought often about this distinction between self-interest and selfishness. Please explain your view of it in greater detail.

Professor Smith Perhaps it would be helpful to consider some familiar examples, Herr Hayek. Think of the great moral leaders of the 20th century, including the Reverend Martin Luther King and Mother Teresa. Neither sought riches. Both, however, accepted large sums of money when they were awarded their Nobel Prizes. Why? Were they *secretly* greedy, and merely found out in the end? I do not think so. They accepted prize money to use it as a resource for support of their moral causes. In this they are not alone. People who run churches, schools, hospitals, and charities all seek resources. Is that greedy? Knowing that people are motivated in part by money tells us nothing about their character.

Professor Heller Many people, Professor Smith, are unaccustomed to the idea that those who do not work in business are nonetheless self-interested.

Professor Smith Dr. Heller! For years now I have admired your academic scholarship and your service to the U.S. government. I hope you found self-satisfaction in each endeavor. I am sure you did. It is human nature to be self-interested. People act in accordance with their self-interest whether they give to others or give to themselves. Nurses tend to the sick to earn an income, of course, but also because of the satisfaction they gain from their work. Scientists do research, in part, to earn income, but also because of the satisfaction they gain in their efforts to learn something new.

Professor Keynes Years ago I maintained friendships with many writers and artists in and around London, and I can vouch for the fact that they showed ample self-interest in their work. Some observers regarded these people, however, as self-absorbed idlers. Yet you contend that those who act in their own self-interest — businesspeople and others — actually serve the common good. Would you please say more about that?

Professor Smith I have no doubt, Lord Keynes, that some of your acquaintances in the Bloomsbury group were more than a little difficult to get on with. Yet it is true that the common good is furthered by the self-interested action of individuals. Think of the millions of honest, mutually satisfying exchanges that occur every day in the U.S. market economy. Business people, acting in regard to their self-interest, produce the goods and services that consumers wish to purchase.

continued on next page  

Think of all the products people have used to their advantage in your 20th century that did not exist in my 18th century! It is people's regard for their own self-interest that makes such achievement across the centuries possible.

Professor Marx I fear you live in a dream world of abstraction, Professor Smith. People of low moral character will surely take advantage of any system that seeks the public good as a product of self-interested behavior.

Professor Smith In my time-travel scholarship, Herr Marx, I have read much about what people today refer to as gaming the system, and I know that it has been an irresistible temptation for many. In fact it seemed especially attractive throughout much of the 20th century in a nation whose rulers tried to fashion an economy according to your theories. Of course capitalists have also been among those seeking to use market systems unscrupulously. Market systems provide safeguards against such opportunism, but the safeguards do not depend on people's good intentions; they rely instead on competition. Market systems must be able to encourage competition among producers. The fear of competition is what pushes business people to respect the wishes of their customers. If they don't, another business person will. That prospect — of losing profits, income, perhaps one's entire business investment — does more than laws and regulations to encourage business people to act properly with regard to their customers.

Professor Locke It is a far-reaching claim that you make, Professor Smith. You seem almost to be saying that market systems help to develop good character even though good character is not their crucial safeguard of proper conduct.

Professor Smith I would go further: It is the absence of markets that encourages immoral behavior.

Professor Locke Admirably blunt and plain-spoken. Please say more, since your view will strike many as suspect.

Professor Smith Of course. The values of the market include honesty. While markets are vulnerable occasionally to scam artists and schemers, business people know that customers eventually will punish those who cheat and lie to them. Business people who are rogues and scoundrels usually wind up bankrupt or in jail. Markets also encourage tolerance. Business people who discriminate in hiring or refuse to sell to all paying customers will eventually find themselves punished in an extra-judicial manner: by not finding the best employee for the job or by earning less in sales, for example. I could go on. Other values encouraged by markets include cooperation, courtesy, and enterprise.

Professor Ricardo On which would you rather depend, Professor Smith: people who do good out of a sense of caring or people who do good out of a sense of self-interest?

Professor Smith Caring is a fine trait, to be sure, so far as it goes, but people tend to care especially for family members and others who are well known to them. I have been interested by contrast in conduct in the large, public world, where strangers must interact with one another and hope not to be cheated or harmed. In that arena, people who earn an income by selling goods and services help to establish, almost without noticing that they are doing so, important norms of conduct. Acting in their own interest as business people, they help others who may be complete strangers — people of different beliefs, races, and religions. Many among us would find it difficult to do good for strangers on a similar scale — if doing good depended merely on an ethic of benevolence or care. The record of experience shows that people will more often do the right thing when they act in regard to self-interest.

continued on next page   

Professor Say Philosophers in my country have given much thought to the self — to individual consciousness. Please explain your view as to how people will know what their self-interest is, when it comes to producing or buying goods and services?

Professor Smith I have been flattered, M. Say, by the attention you have paid to my work. Market economies provide a signal that tells people what goods and services are worth. This signal is the market price. Prices reflect the value of a good to society and the cost to society of making the good. People in households and businesses use prices in making decisions about what and when to buy and what and when to sell. Market prices register the choices, and thereby reflect the self-interest, of millions of consumers and producers. Most of them are complete strangers to one another, and most have perhaps not engaged at great length in introspection about their individual consciousness.

Panel Moderator I wish to thank Professor Smith and the rest of the panel for speaking with us today.

Professor Smith Thank you, sir. And did you, by chance, find my eyeglasses?

Panel Moderator I am sorry, sir, but your people told my people that our scanner did not detect them. Where were you the last time you had them?

Professor Smith I don't recall. I couldn't find things when I lived in my own time. According to your calendar, I must now be more than 200 years old! And where do you suppose I put my keys? I don't suppose that your people could talk to … .

Panel Moderator I am sorry, Professor Smith; that is all the time we have today.

QUESTIONS FOR DISCUSSION

A. Who was Adam Smith?

____

____

____

B. What is the difference between self-interest and selfishness?

____

____

____

C. What virtues are encouraged in market systems, according to Professor Smith?

____

____

____

D. Why are market prices important?

____

____

____

E. Solve the mystery: How can people acting in their own self-interest contribute to the social good?

____

____

____

____

____

Unit 4, Lesson 21

Activity 1

Diminishing Marginal Returns and the Demand for Labor

The law of diminishing marginal returns states that ***as more of a variable resource is added to a fixed resource, the marginal (additional) output from the variable resource will eventually decline.***

What does this mean? If you were making greeting cards and you only had one scissors and two markers, these resources would be *fixed*. But if you could hire as many workers as you wanted, labor would be a *variable* resource. Your output would be the greeting cards. If you add more workers to the fixed number of scissors and markers, soon there wouldn't be enough scissors and markers to go around. Things would get crowded, and worker productivity would fall as you continued to add workers.

The law of diminishing marginal returns has important implications for business decisions such as how many workers to hire. To see this, look at the following example of a class's greeting card production. Use the information to answer the questions that follow.

1. Number of Workers	2. Number of Cards Produced	3. Marginal Product of Labor	4. Value of Marginal Product (Price = $2)
0	0	---	---
1	4	4	$8
2	9	5	$10
3	15		
4	20		
5	24		
6	26		
7	27		
8	27		

1. The **Marginal Product of Labor** is the additional output from adding one more worker. When there were 0 workers, 0 cards were produced. When there was one worker, 4 cards were produced. Therefore the marginal product of the first worker was 4. When a second worker was added, the number of cards produced went up to nine. The marginal (additional) output from the second worker was 5 (9 minus 4).

   A. Use this idea to fill in the rest of the third column.

   B. With which worker does diminishing marginal returns first occur?

   ______________________________.

   Hint: diminishing marginal returns set in when the marginal product of labor falls. Use this idea to fill in the rest of the fourth column.

2. The **Value of the Marginal Product** refers to the revenue the business would earn from selling the additional cards made by each worker. Let's say the cards would sell for $2 each. Therefore, the value of the cards produced by the first worker would be $8 ($4 times 2 cards). The value of the cards produced by the second worker would be $10 ($2 times 5 cards).

3. **How Many Workers Should You Hire?** The economic way of thinking says that when you are deciding whether to do something, you should compare the marginal benefits to the marginal costs. If the marginal benefits are greater, do it! If the marginal costs are greater, don't do it. Let's apply this idea to the decision of whether or not to hire one more worker to make greeting cards. Assume that the greeting card firm is interested in making as much profit as possible.

Marginal Cost: Assume that the only cost the business has is paying its workers; everything else has been donated. The cost of hiring each worker for the time period involved is $5. That is, the marginal cost of hiring another worker is $5.

Marginal Benefit: From column four we know the value that each worker would bring to the business if he or she were hired. In this example, the marginal revenue product gives the marginal benefit of hiring each worker.

Thinking at the Margin: The first worker brings in $8 in revenue, and would cost the firm $5. Would the firm hire this worker? Of course. Hiring this worker would add $3 to the firm's profit. Would the firm hire the second worker? Yes: the second worker would bring in $10 in revenue while costing the firm $5, so hiring the second worker would be profitable also. Do this same analysis for additional workers until you reach a point where it is no longer profitable to hire another worker.

- How many workers would the business be willing to hire at the rate of $5? ________

Unit 4, Lesson 22

Activity 1

Examples of Four Models of Market Structure

1. Pure Competition and Cucumbers

The U.S. agriculture industry comes close to approximating what economists mean when they talk about an industry in *pure* or *perfect competition.* There are many (more than two million) farms in the United States. Because this number is so high, it is unlikely that any one farmer could set, or influence, overall farm prices. To make this clearer, let's focus on a certain farm product: cucumbers.

Several states including Michigan, Mississippi, Ohio, Iowa, Florida, New York, Wisconsin, and Indiana list cucumbers among their major agricultural crops. In addition to those who grow cucumbers to sell to others, many people grow them in home gardens for their own use. It is relatively easy to begin growing cucumbers. They thrive in many types of soil and require temperatures of about 65-75 degrees Fahrenheit, commonly found throughout the United States in summer months. Cucumbers grow quickly; they are generally ready to harvest about two months from the time of planting.

Let's assume that you decide to enter the cucumber industry by growing cucumbers in your back yard to sell at a local farmers' market. Although there are different varieties of cucumbers, your cucumbers will most likely be very similar, if not identical, to others for sale in your area. If the going price at the farmers' market is, say, three cucumbers for a dollar, and you try to sell yours for a higher price, you probably won't sell any at all. If you decide to take your cucumbers off the market, the decrease in overall supply won't be enough to cause the going price to rise. You are unable to control the price because there are so many other producers. And it probably wouldn't be profitable for you to try to use non-price competition (such as advertising) to convince people to pay a higher price for your cucumbers, since your cucumbers and your neighbors' are virtually identical.

In addition to the market for many agricultural products, another example of markets that have some characteristics of pure competition is the market for foreign exchange (foreign currency). Foreign exchange markets have large numbers of sellers selling identical products, and it is usually the case that no one seller can influence the going price. It is relatively easy to enter the industry, and non-price competition generally does not exist.

2. Monopolistic Competition and Your Haircut

If the place where you live is like many other places in the United States, you and your friends have many choices about where to go to get a haircut. The price you pay for a basic haircut probably ranges from a few dollars at a discount establishment to many dollars at an upscale salon. Since there are so many hair stylists, why doesn't competition drive the prices down so that all haircuts cost the same price?

The answer has to do with the type of market structure referred to as *monopolistic competition*. Hair stylists and many other local businesses such as gas stations, fast-food restaurants, and dry cleaners are similar in many ways to purely competitive markets. There are many competing sellers or firms in the industry, and it is relatively easy to open a business of this type. But in monopolistic competition sellers try to convince customers that their products are different from those of other sellers, and they compete with each other in ways other than by lowering prices.

Some people (your parents, if they are paying your bills) might argue that one hair cut is much like another, so why pay one person $60 if you can pay someone else $7? The more expensive hair stylists might respond by claiming that they do better work and know the latest styles, and their haircuts are therefore different from the cheaper ones. Because these hair stylists convince their customers that their haircuts are different, they are able to influence the prices they charge. They do not have to charge the same price every other hair stylist in town charges.

Firms such as hair salons often compete with one another by engaging in *non-price competition*. They may attract more customers because they have a better location, or because they have more appealing surroundings or more convenient hours. The existence of non-price competition is widespread under monopolistic competition. You can probably think of many examples of how local fast-food restaurants and gas stations compete in ways other than by charging lower prices.

In summary, firms in monopolistic competition have some characteristics that are similar to pure competition, and some characteristics that are similar to pure monopolies. But all in all, they are much more competitive than they are monopolistic.

3. Oligopoly and Breakfast Cereals

Oligopoly means that there are a few firms in an industry. A firm in an oligopolistic industry may produce products that differ from those produced by others in the industry (one soap or cereal different from

continued on next page   

other soaps or cereals, for example), or it may produce products that are virtually identical to products produced by others (copper or glass, for example). Because there are only a few producers, sellers may have significant control over the prices they charge. Because of their small numbers, firms in oligopoly also must pay careful attention to the prices charged by their competitors. For example, if one airline lowers its prices, chances are others will follow. Because oligopolistic firms are often very large companies, it is often difficult for new firms to enter the industry and compete with the existing firms.

One way to determine whether an industry is an oligopoly is to look at the *concentration ratio* for the industry: the percentage of total output produced by the largest firms. According to data released by the U.S. Census in mid 2001, the four largest breakfast cereal companies (Kellogg, General Mills, Post, and Quaker) were producing over 86 percent of the total amount of breakfast cereals in the United States. The breakfast cereal industry is considered to be highly concentrated and is therefore an oligopoly.

As you have no doubt noticed, cereal producers spend a lot on advertising and use advertising as a way to compete with one another. This expensive form of non-price competition is common in oligopolistic industries that have differentiated products. Other examples of this type of oligopoly are cars, soaps, and airlines. Because advertising on a national scale is so expensive, this is a cost factor that serves to keep competitors out of the industry.

When there are only a few major producers in the industry, there is a possibility of *collusion*. That is, the firms may get together to try to set prices illegally. Therefore, oligopolies frequently come under the scrutiny of government regulatory agencies such as the Federal Trade Commission (FTC). The FTC investigated the cereal industry in the 1970s and 1980s, but the case was eventually discontinued without action to break up the major companies. And of course, just because there are only a few major producers in an industry does not mean that collusion exists. A few firms can compete with each other as fiercely as a large number of firms.

4. Monopoly and Diamonds

The definition of *monopoly* is fairly easy: A monopoly exists if there is a single seller of a unique product. Coming up with real-life examples of monopolies is not so easy, because most businesses have competition of some sort. If you run the only pizza restaurant in a small town, do you have a monopoly, or do you compete with other types of restaurants? Is the U.S. Postal Service a monopoly, or does it compete with UPS and FedEx? Are professional sports teams in effect geographic monopolies, or do they compete with other forms of entertainment? Economists frequently observe that unless monopolies are sanctioned and protected by governments, or unless they engage in illegal use of force, they tend to self-destruct due to competitive forces. Patents are an example of the means by which a government can sanction a monopoly. The diamond industry is an example of a monopoly that broke up because of its inability to control competition.

Beginning in the 1930s and throughout most of the 20th century, the De Beers company, based in Switzerland and South Africa, controlled most of the world's diamond supply. De Beers provides a good example of a monopoly. Control of the supply of diamonds enabled De Beers to restrict the number of diamonds offered for sale and sell them at higher prices than would exist under competition. To be a monopoly, a company must have strong *barriers to entry* — that is, ways to keep competitors out of the industry. Over the years, De Beers eliminated its competition principally by buying up all the rough diamonds available. De Beers dealt with potential problems of increasing supply and falling prices by buying and stockpiling diamonds in its London vaults when prices were low and selling them when prices were high. De Beers used non-price competition in the form of advertising ("A Diamond is Forever") to try to keep demand high and to reinforce its brand name.

Toward the end of the century, De Beers began to lose its monopoly control. An Australian diamond producing company chose to withdraw from the monopoly. Russia, although still officially part of the monopoly, began to sell diamonds directly to other countries rather than to De Beers. And discoveries of diamonds in Canada and Africa made it harder for De Beers to control the supply. Ethical issues involved with buying diamonds from warring African countries led to more problems for De Beers. Therefore, in July 2000, De Beers announced that it would no longer attempt to control the world's supply of diamonds, and the monopoly officially ended.

Although cases of pure monopoly are rare, existence of near monopolies may pose problems for an economy. Monopolies exercise strong control over their prices and may have little incentive to be efficient and innovative. In the United States, monopolies are not illegal, but actions firms take to preserve their monopoly are. Monopolies can be prosecuted under antitrust laws, such as occurred with Microsoft in 2000. In other cases, the government may regulate the monopoly, as occurs with many public utilities.

Unit 4, Lesson 22

Activity 2

Characteristics of Four Market Structures

Directions: Fill in the table below, using the information provided by Activity 1.

	Market Characteristics					
Type of Market	**Number of Firms in Industry**	**Similar or Different Products**	**Ability to Control Prices**	**Ease of Entering the Industry**	**Existence of Non-Price Competition**	**Examples**
Pure Competition						
Monopolistic Competition						
Oligopoly						
Monopoly						

Unit 4, Lesson 23

Activity 1

Andrea's Software Business

Andrea has developed a computer software program that she calls *The Homework Helper*. She has programmed in assignments, group projects, and textbook readings for all her classes, as well as relevant Web sites and related on-line research resources. Her program notifies her when assignments are due and exams are coming up, and it also reminds her of school activities, parties, dates for sending in college applications, and birthdays of friends and relatives. And it plays her favorite songs while she works. Ten of Andrea's friends have told her that they would each be willing to pay her $56 if she would set up and adapt her program for them. Andrea could use a little extra money and would like to help out her friends (but maybe not all of them). She is also interested in starting a small computer consulting business and thinks this would be a good way to begin.

Total Fixed Costs: Andrea already paid $60 to her city for a license to operate a small business. Therefore, no matter how many software programs she sells (zero to ten), she has *fixed costs* of $60.

Total Variable Costs: Andrea estimates that some costs, including the cost of disks and paying herself an hourly wage for her time, will change depending on how many programs she decides to produce. She considers her wages to be a cost (an opportunity cost) because if she produces software, she gives up similar wages that she could earn in another job. Andrea's estimates of her *variable costs* are shown in the third column in Activity 2. For example, if she produces no software, she has no variable costs. For one program, her variable costs would be $45. Her variable costs for two programs would be a total of $85, and so on.

Total Costs: Andrea's *total costs* for producing different quantities of software are the sum of her fixed costs and variable costs. For example, if she produces no software, she has total costs of $60, because her fixed costs are $60 and her variable costs are $0. If she produces nine software programs, her total costs are $450 ($60 fixed costs plus $390 variable costs).

Marginal Costs: Andrea's *marginal costs* are the costs of producing one more software program. Another way of saying this is that marginal costs are how much total costs (or total variable costs) change when she produces one more software program. For example, if Andrea produces no software, her total costs are $60. If she produces one software program, her total costs go up to $105. Therefore, the marginal cost, or additional cost, of producing one software program is $45 ($105 minus $60). Can you explain why the marginal cost of the tenth software program is $75?

Price: Andrea's ten friends have indicated that they are willing to pay her $56 each for her software program. Therefore, the price for each program is $56.

Total Revenue: *Total revenue* is the amount of money a business takes in from selling a good or service. Therefore, it is the selling price times the amount sold. For example, if Andrea sells nine software programs at a price of $56 each, her total revenue is $504 (nine times $56).

Marginal Revenue: *Marginal revenue* is the additional revenue Andrea would take in if she sold one more software program. For example, if she sells no software, her total revenue is $0. If she sells one program her total revenue is $56. Therefore, the marginal revenue of selling one software program is $56 ($56 minus 0). Do you notice a relationship between marginal revenue and price in this example?

Profit: *Profit* is defined as a firm's total revenues minus its total costs. If total costs are greater than total revenues, the firm makes losses. For example, if Andrea produces no software, she has losses of $60 because her total revenue is $0 and her total costs are $60.

Directions: Your goal is to help Andrea decide exactly how many software programs to produce and sell to make the most profit possible. Use the information provided to:

- fill in all the blank spaces in the chart on Activity 2, and
- answer the questions on Activity 2 below the chart.

The first column on the chart lists the number of software programs that Andrea is considering selling, ranging from zero to 10. The other columns show the various costs, revenues, and profits or losses she would make depending on how many programs she decides to sell.

When you have finished Activity 2, think about the following ***Rules for Economic Decision Making.***

RULES FOR ECONOMIC DECISION MAKING:

- *General rule for Andrea to make the most profit:* ***If the marginal revenue of producing one more program is greater than the marginal cost, she should produce it! If the marginal cost is greater than the marginal revenue, she should not produce it.***
- *General rule for making decisions:* ***If the marginal benefits of doing something are greater than the marginal costs, do it! If the marginal costs are greater than the marginal benefits, don't do it.***

Unit 4, Lesson 23

Activity 2

Andrea's Software Business: Do the Math

Number of Programs	Total Fixed Costs	Total Variable Costs	Total Costs	Marginal Costs	Price	Total Revenue	Marginal Revenue	Profit (or Loss)
0	$60	$0	$60	---	---	0	---	-$60 (loss)
1		$45	$105	$45	$56	$56	$56	
2		$85		$40				
3	$60	$120					$56	-$12 (loss)
4		$150						
5		$185			$56			
6	$60	$225						$51 (profit)
7		$270					$56	
8		$325			$56			
9		$390	$450			$504		
10		$465		$75				

A. How many software programs should Andrea sell to make the most profit? __________
What would her profit be? __________

What is the marginal revenue for this number of programs? __________
The marginal cost? __________

B. If Andrea sold one more software program than your answer to Part A, what would her profit be? __________

What is the marginal revenue for this number of programs? __________
The marginal cost? __________

UNIT 5

THE VISIBLE HAND: THE ROLE OF GOVERNMENT IN A MARKET ECONOMY

Lesson 24

- Activity 1 Externalities: How Actions Affect Others
- Activity 2 The Vanishing Wildlife Mystery

Lesson 25

- Activity 1 The Economics of the U.S. Constitution
- Activity 2 An Examination of the Economic Features of the U.S. Constitution

Lesson 26

- Activity 1 Public versus Private Goods

Lesson 27

- Activity 1 The Economics of Special Interest Groups

Lesson 29

- Activity 1 What Is a Fair Tax?
- Activity 2 The National Commission of Taxation Makes Its Annual Forecasts

Unit 5, Lesson 24

Activity 1

Externalities: How Actions Affect Others

People sometimes make private decisions that have an unintended impact on others. These are called external effects. They occur when one person or group does something that affects other people without the usual costs or payments.

There are many examples. Drivers sometimes lower their car windows and crank up the radio, blaring the music. At no cost to such drivers, they are imposing their music on innocent people who may not want to listen to it. A student might be trying to do homework in the school library while others seated at a nearby table talk incessantly. At no cost to them, the talkers are imposing their conversation on the innocent student.

Businesses sometimes act in a similar fashion. When businesses are deciding what to produce and how to produce it, they consider only their internal costs — the costs to the firm. They do not take account of costs that might be imposed on others. These are called externalities. Externalities are of two sorts.

A negative externality harms others. Air, land, and water pollution are common examples. When a business dumps waste into a river, for example, it saves money by using the river, in effect, as a free waste-disposal service. However, people who wish to use the river for recreation or for drinking water are harmed.

A positive externality helps others. Education is widely regarded as a positive externality. Education helps not only the people being educated; it helps all of us. An educated person can more easily get a job and is less likely to require expensive forms of support by the government. Compared to those with less education, educated people commit fewer crimes, vote more often, and have lower medical expenses. Government sometimes subsidizes, or provides aid, for activities that create positive externalities, such as education.

Scientific research is also widely regarded as a positive externality. Government and university labs have produced many technological breakthroughs with positive externalities. The development of hybrid seed corn and the Internet are examples.

Paying for Externalities

Markets fail when negative and positive externalities exist and neither party pays for all the costs or all the benefits. A polluting factory and its customers don't pay for all the cost of making or using the products that pollute air or water.

Government, as a regulator, can force businesses and their customers to pay all the costs of production by taxing pollution, imposing direct controls, or demanding that waste be cleaned. However, government actions designed to clean up the environment also have costs. We will see later that in the name of an improved environment, government has pursued some costly programs that have not been effective.

Questions for Discussion

A. What are externalities?

____

____

____

B. Name at least two activities that involve negative externalities.

____

____

____

C. Name at least two activities that involve positive externalities.

____

____

____

D. Why might governments choose to take action when markets produce negative and positive externalities?

____

____

____

E. Many citizens believe that education has positive externalities. Explain why this is so.

____

____

____

Unit 5, Lesson 24

Activity 2

The Vanishing Wildlife Mystery

The mystery in this case has to do with why powerful laws such as the Endangered Species Act (ESA), in operation since 1973, have failed to protect many plants and animals.

Recall the Guide to Economic Reasoning.

1. People choose.
2. People's choices involve costs.
3. People respond to incentives in predictable ways.
4. People create economic systems that influence individual choices and incentives
5. People gain when they trade voluntarily.
6. People's choices have consequences that lie in the future.

Now, let's consider the answers to the True/False questions.

- The government officials who enforce the Endangered Species Act are lazy.

  The answer is *false*. The people who administer the Endangered Species Act are by and large devoted to its mission and work hard in support of it.

- Hundreds of plants and animals remain on the endangered list despite 30 years of legal efforts to help them.

  The answer is *true*. While many plants and animals have been added to the list of Endangered Species, almost none have been removed. We often hear that endangered species decline for two reasons. First, the habitat disappears or changes; second, the species is over-hunted. Both points are important. But economic analysis allows us to look at the problem more deeply.

- Government polices sometimes have unintended consequences.

  The answer is *true*. Some background might help. Consider the passenger pigeon, a bird so common in the nineteenth century that its disappearance is amazing. One naturalist saw a flock in Kentucky that he claimed included more than 2 billion birds. But hunters shot pigeons in huge numbers and shipped them east for sale. Eventually the pigeons disappeared. The last one died in the Cincinnati Zoo in 1914.

  Why were carrier pigeons killed off? They had no protectors. Nobody owned them. Even though many people wanted to preserve them for the future, there was no way for anyone to make sure that they would survive. No one had an incentive to hold back and not kill a pigeon. It only would mean that someone else would kill it.

  Most endangered species face the same problem as the carrier pigeon. To protect endangered species, the government enacted the Endangered Species Act in 1973. The law allows government officials to deny landowners the use of their property if an endangered species is found to be present. This policy has had many unintended results. Most of these had to do with the incentives that resulted from the new law.

- The Endangered Species Act offers incentives that encourage landowners not to cooperate in protecting endangered species.

  The answer is *true*. To understand this, we have to examine how the ESA works. The law makes it illegal to "harass, harm, pursue, hunt, shoot, wound, kill, trap, capture, or collect" or attempt any of these actions in regard to a plant or animal listed on the Endangered Species list. At first glance, this may appear as an excellent idea. After all, don't we wish to discourage landowners from harming endangered species?

  Now let's approach the problem differently, bearing in mind how rules influence incentives and choices. Consider the incentives the law creates for land owners. Imagine that you own 40 acres of land with timber that is 20 years old. You have been planning to wait another 5 to 10 years before harvesting the timber to help pay for your daughter's wedding. Now your neighbor tells you that your trees are the perfect habitat for the endangered silver-nosed squirrel. The squirrel roams widely and needs about 10 acres on which to survive. Some of them have been spotted in a wood lot 50 miles from your land. What do you do? You might well be tempted to harvest your timber right away and set the money aside for the wedding rather than risk losing your ability to harvest a portion of the timber as would be the case if the law were applied to protect the squirrel.

  The ESA creates incentives that encourage landowners, people who normally take good care of what they own, to destroy habitat. Fearing that they might be "caught" with an endangered species on their land gives landowners an incentive to destroy the habitat before it becomes unavailable to them. By presenting perverse incentives to land owners, the ESA generates costs that may exceed the benefits gained in the protection of endangered species.

continued on next page   

QUESTIONS FOR DISCUSSION

A. What is the Endangered Species Act?

____

____

____

B. What were the goals of the act?

____

____

____

C. Why were the carrier pigeons destroyed?

____

____

____

D. Why does the Endangered Species Act appear to be a government failure?

____

____

____

Unit 5, Lesson 25

Activity 1

The Economics of the U.S. Constitution

by Douglass C. North

It is now over two hundred years since the Constitutional Convention drafted the U.S. Constitution. That document thus is one of the most durable sources of rules in all of history. However, its origins and its significance have been and continue to be a source of controversy. In the essay, I shall try to provide some tentative answers to the following questions. 1) How did the Constitution come to be written as it is? 2) Whose interests were served by the document? 3) What does it say? 4) How important was it at the time and for subsequent generations? 5) What are the lessons to be learned with respect to calling a new constitutional convention to rewrite it?

HOW DID THE CONSTITUTION COME TO BE WRITTEN AS IT IS?

It is not often that people get a chance to shape their own history from the ground up. Usually we think of history evolving in an incremental way, through the choices and decisions of people as they stem one from another through time. But the Constitutional Convention that followed the creation of the new nation certainly presented the opportunity for its convenors to create an entirely new set of rules. However, both the past and the issues of the time provided constraints. The ideas embodied in the Constitution were forged in the struggle between Parliament and the Crown in the revolutionary 17th Century in England, by the charters of the colonies, and by the ideas that were current in 18th Century England.

The year 1776 produced not one but two documents of historically significant importance to the new nation. One, of course, was the Declaration of Independence. The other was Adam Smith's *Wealth of Nations*. In the course of writing what has come to be thought of as the foundation stone of modern economics, Smith inveighed against the evils of the system that he perceived had dominated England and Europe up to that time, a system he called mercantilism. Mercantilism was a system in which the government was deeply involved in the operation of the economy, providing subsidies, bounties, and monopolistic privileges to individual companies through the assignment of exclusive privileges and trading rights. Adam Smith felt that mercantilism was an inefficient system that fostered monopoly. In contrast, Smith argued that the main basis for economic growth and efficiency was specialization and division of labor. Efficiency came from specialization in the production and distribution process. He argued that by allowing each person to concentrate on doing just one thing repetitively, goods could be produced more rapidly and efficiently. He believed that competition in the market would force people to become more efficient and would encourage improvements in technology and productive expansion. Thus, rather than artificial inducements to produce (bounty and subsidy), Smith believed that free markets, which valued the relative gains of producing different kinds of things, provided the proper incentives for productive economic activity.

The conflict between Adam Smith's view and the traditional mercantilist view was certainly much in the minds of the Americans in the 1780s as they struggled to resolve the many problems they faced. Separated from England, they no longer enjoyed the privileges of operating within her Navigation Acts, which had assured the colonies protected markets against foreign competition. Moreover, at home they faced huge debts accumulated in the course of the Revolutionary War (including the problem of paying the soldiers of the Revolutionary War who had been promised substantial benefits), the need to raise taxes to operate government, and the need to provide protection to traders against Barbary Pirates in the Mediterranean.

And it was not just the ideas and the issues of the time that turned out to be decisive for this remarkable document. An extraordinary concatenation of events also affected it. Initially the Convention was called simply to overhaul the Articles of Confederation. The convenors were heavily loaded in favor of federalists rather than anti-federalists. Many anti-federalists believed that the Convention would be a failure and that they could do very little to improve conditions; thus, they simply would have nothing to do with it. What actually happened was quite different. The views of the convenors turned out to be in near unanimity with respect to what ought to be done, and in short order they wrote a completely new constitution. Contrary to the anti-federalists, the federalists believed the new nation was in crisis and that in the absence of a new constitution it could not be held together. To assure and speed ratification, they suggested amendments to the Constitution that would be undertaken as soon as the new Constitution came into existence and the first Congress had been convened. Thus, the Bill of Rights was actually guaranteed in the course of the ratification controversy; in fact, it was essential for the success of ratification. As a result, the anti-federalists, who foresaw failure at the Convention and failure in the ratification process, were confronted instead with a feasible document, which, with the additional guarantee of the Bill of Rights, also became a document that was ratified and that provided the basic rules of the new nation.

continued on next page  

WHOSE INTERESTS WERE SERVED BY THE DOCUMENT?

Was the Constitution a class document written narrowly in the interests of a small group? This controversy has existed ever since Charles Beard's celebrated book, entitled *The Economic Interpretation of the Constitution*, asked whether the Constitution reflected the disembodied wisdom of a group of disinterested individuals or a narrower set of interests of its framers. Put that way, the question is not a very interesting one. Surely the framers of the Constitution devised it in such a way that it was consistent with their long-run interests, but surely also their view was that it must be a viable political and economic document that could enable a nation to survive and thrive. In fact a major issue that shaped the writing of the Constitution was a concern with factions or interest groups of citizens bent on using the political process to further their own well-being. The most durable source of faction was the unequal distribution of wealth and income. In one of the most celebrated essays ever written in political theory, Federalist Paper No. 10 (written to support ratification), Madison argued that the aim of the constitutional convenors was to prevent factions from controlling the political system and using it in their interests. The Constitution did not make everyone equal. Some states did impose property qualifications in order to vote and therefore excluded the poorest members of society. Moreover, it is clear that the Constitution made it more costly to redistribute wealth from the rich to the poor than vice versa. Yet, it is equally obvious that this was not the prime consideration of the makers of the Constitution. The prime consideration, if we take Madison at his word, was to make all redistributive efforts by factions (of whatever kind) costly and to provide a framework that would encourage productive pursuits instead of redistributive efforts.

WHAT DOES THE CONSTITUTION SAY?

Overall, a major design of the Constitution, as the foregoing paragraph suggests, was to provide a set of checks and balances in the political process, so that no faction could, in short order, get control of the reins of government and redistribute wealth and income in their favor. This was done by providing for separate legislative, executive, and judicial bodies, each with checks upon the other, each with distinct and separate powers. State and federal government powers were also separated. There is no doubt that this federal form of government was an important source of decentralization in the political process and that it certainly raised the costs of an interest group coming to control the political process.

Now let's turn to specific economic issues. The Constitution enabled the federal government to levy taxes (an essential function of government if it is to survive), and to coin money and regulate its value. It gave the federal government authority over foreign affairs, including the negotiation of tariffs and treaties. It gave the federal government the right to regulate interstate commerce, thus prohibiting the states from erecting barriers to the interstate movement of goods, but also permitting the federal government to impose its own rules upon interstate commerce.

Certainly the more important contribution of the Constitution was that it established a framework for the efficient conduct of economic affairs. It defined the protection of private property and specified that contracts would be enforced; it stipulated rules for bankruptcy, an important element since bankruptcy implies a failure to live up to contracts. In short, it created a system of well specified property rights, which reduced uncertainty and permitted the development of free markets — essential, in Adam Smith's view, for a productive economy.

QUESTIONS FOR DISCUSSION

A. How did Adam Smith, through his book *The Wealth of Nations*, influence the writers of the Constitution?

____

____

____

B. In North's view, was the Constitution a document written to protect the interests of the founders?

____

____

____

C. Why is it difficult under the Constitution for factions or interest groups to redistribute income from rich to poor or poor to rich?

____

____

____

continued on next page   

D. What specific economic powers does the constitution confer on the federal government?

____

____

____

____

____

E. Why might Adam Smith have approved of the U.S. Constitution?

____

____

____

____

____

Unit 5, Lesson 25

Activity 2

An Examination of the Economic Features of the U.S. Constitution

Directions: Below is a chart that allows you to identify the "economic articles" of the U.S. Constitution. Obtain a copy of the U.S. Constitution and answer the following questions; specify where in the Constitution you found the information.

Question	Answer	Where is it in the Constitution?
1. How does the Constitution make it difficult for interest groups or factions to redistribute wealth?	The U.S Constitution establishes three branches of government that form a system of checks and balances, making it difficult for one interest group or faction to dominate.	
2. In what body must bills for raising revenue originate?	House of Representatives	
3. The writers insisted that taxes should be levied with the consent of the governed. Who has the power to levy and collect taxes and duties?		
4. Who has the power to coin money?		
5. What branch of government regulates business?		
6. Some governments allow scientists to "own" their ideas for a period of time, to create an incentive for research. May writers and inventors be granted copyrights to protect their ideas? Explain.		
7. The United States created an internal "free trade zone" among the states. May states levy taxes on exports or imports? Explain.		
8. Contracts are an important means of protection for private property. They require that people hold to their financial commitments. Courts enforce contracts. Does the federal government have the authority to abolish contracts? Explain.		
9. What branch of government has the power to make and ratify treaties?		
10. Does "due process of law" (the government must follow certain steps or procedures specified by the law) apply to private ownership of property? Explain.		
11. Can people be forced to work for others without compensation? Explain.		

Unit 5, Lesson 26

Activity 1

Public versus Private Goods

PART 1: THE PUBLIC SECTOR AND THE PRIVATE SECTOR

The public sector of the economy is all the production and consumption activities of government. One important economic role of the public sector is to produce goods and services. This might surprise you. We usually think of goods and services as being produced in the marketplace or what is often called the private sector of the economy. After all, in a market economy, people provide the goods and services for which others are willing to pay.

A private good or service conveys its benefits only to the purchaser. Most goods and services are private. They include the CD you just purchased or that car your friend just bought. Nevertheless, private sector suppliers may not produce certain goods and service in sufficient quantities, even though large numbers of people may want them.

Which goods and services might these be? What are these things that will not be produced in sufficient quantity even though many people want them? These are public goods. Public goods or services convey benefits to payers and non-payers. They tend to be the goods and services that become available to everyone once they are produced — whether people pay for them or not. If individuals can obtain a good or service whether they pay for it or not, they have less incentive to pay. They are tempted to become "free riders."

Similarly, if producers anticipate that the goods or services they produce will be "given away" to non-payers or free riders, they have little incentive to produce. That is why the private sector may not produce enough — or any — of certain goods or services that people want.

PUBLIC GOODS AND SERVICES HAVE TWO, VERY SIMILAR CHARACTERISTICS:

1. Non-exclusion: If it is difficult to exclude non-payers from receiving some goods or services, the government should probably produce them. For example, a streetlight on a public street would benefit all the neighbors, regardless of how many had paid for it.
2. Shared consumption: If one person's use or consumption of a good or service does not reduce its usefulness to others, the government should probably produce that good or service. For example, national defense tends to benefit or be shared by everyone, and its benefit to one person does not diminish its benefit to another.

Of course, some goods and services may be produced in both the public and the private sectors. While our society may view particular goods or services as meeting the tests of non-exclusion and shared consumption, this may not prevent the good or service from being offered by the private sector for consumers who do wish to pay for it individually. For example, there are private schools as well as public schools, private camping sites as well as public camping sites, and, in some places, private means for garbage collection as well as public means for garbage collection.

QUESTIONS FOR DISCUSSION

A. What is the public sector?

____

____

____

B. What is the private sector?

____

____

____

C. What makes a private good unique?

____

____

____

D. What makes a public good or service different from a private good or service?

____

____

____

continued on next page 

E. What is a "free rider"?

____

____

____

F. What does non-exclusion mean?

____

____

____

G. What is shared consumption?

____

____

____

PART 2: CLASSIFYING GOODS AND SERVICES

Column 1 in the chart below shows a list of goods and services. Practice your understanding of the concepts of non-exclusion and shared consumption and decide whether each item is best classified as one that should be produced by government or one that should be produced by private business. State in column 2 whether the public sector, private sector, or both should produce the good or service. Briefly in column 3 explain your choice. Be careful. The distinctions are not always neat and easy.

1. Good or Service	2. Public? Private? Both?	3. Why? Can non-payers be excluded? Does consumption by one person reduce usefulness for another?
Police		
Flood control		
Gourmet coffee shops		
High school education		
Movie tickets		
Severe weather warning system		
Laptop computer		

Unit 5, Lesson 27

Activity 1

The Economics of Special Interest Groups

Part 1: Who Will Catch the Muskies?

The citizens of Twin Lakes (population 4 million) have been big supporters of professional baseball for several years. On opening day their team, the Muskies, always sets the attendance record for the major leagues. But lately it has become clear that the people of Twin Lakes will have problems keeping the home team at home. The Twin Lakes Baseball Park, the "Home of the Muskies," is getting old. It provides inadequate parking, and the stadium itself--one that seemed great to most fans 30 years ago--now seems dingy, cramped, and lacking in luxury amenities. It has also become expensive to operate. Sensing dissatisfaction, leaders in three other cities with modern ball parks are talking to the owners of the Muskies, urging them to relocate and find a new home for the team, in a new city and a new stadium.

Many special interests in Twin Lakes are deeply concerned. Labor and business groups are distressed about the loss of jobs they would suffer if the Muskies were to move. For example, hotel and restaurant owners and their employee unions depend heavily on income generated by the Muskies. Local government leaders are worried about the loss of tax revenue that would follow if the team were to leave; they are also worried about being left with an empty "dinosaur" stadium. The local fan organization, the Musky Mongers, is obviously worried because one of its favorite pastimes is feeling threatened. One fan was overheard saying, "If the Muskies move, I'm moving with them!"

Facing these threats, the interest groups have worked out a plan with a coalition of city, county, and state government leaders. Their idea is to build a new stadium on land originally intended for an industrial park. The new stadium will cost $400 million. Groups representing the Muskies, local businesses, labor, and fans strongly back the new stadium idea. Together they have obtained tentative commitments for local and state funding totaling $350 million.

On April 5, the date of the season's home opener, all the interest groups (business, labor, fans, state and local governments) urged the state's 14 members of the U.S. House of Representatives and its two U.S. Senators to lobby for $50 million in federal funds to allow them to obtain all the funds needed to complete the new stadium.

ANSWER THE FOLLOWING QUESTIONS:

A. Who will benefit from the construction of the new stadium?

____

____

____

B. Will people in other states and communities derive much benefit from the construction of the new stadium? Why or why not?

____

____

____

C. If you knew that your taxes would increase by a few cents so the people in Twin Lakes could have a new stadium, would you protest the action to your members of Congress? Why or why not?

____

____

____

D. What do you predict will happen in this situation? (Think about who benefits, who pays, and the incentives at stake for the members of Congress from the state.)

____

____

____

continued on next page 

Unit 5, Lesson 27

Activity 1

Part 2: Who Ever Heard of Townsend?

The people in Houston, Texas, want to obtain federal funding to help pay for a modern subway system. The people in Townsend, Wisconsin (population about 500), want to have a new federal dam and reservoir constructed in their area. By reference to Houston and Townsend, answer the following questions:

- **The Houston Subway**

A. Who will benefit from construction of the new subway?

B. Will people in other states and communities derive much benefit?

C. What do you predict will happen?

- **The Townsend Dam and Reservoir**

A. Who will benefit from the construction of the new dam and reservoir?

B. Will people in other states and communities derive much benefit?

C. What do you predict will happen?

Unit 5, Lesson 29

Activity 1

What Is a Fair Tax?

PART 1: THE CRITERIA

1. ***Ability to Pay:*** A fair tax should equally tax individuals with equal ability to pay. People with different amounts of wealth or income should pay different amounts of taxes. A proportional tax (sometimes called a flat tax) takes the same percentage of income of wealth from all taxpayers. A progressive tax means that those with higher incomes or those who are wealthier pay a higher proportion of their income in taxes. A regressive tax means that poor people pay a higher proportion of their income in taxes than those with higher income or those who are wealthier. Income tax policy in the United States has generally reflected the idea that a progressive tax is fair. However, interest in proportional taxes in commonly expressed.
2. ***Efficiency:*** A fair tax should not inhibit productive activities. It should not discourage people from working or investing in new businesses. It should not encourage individuals to be wasteful in buying goods because of their tax benefits rather than their value. A fair tax should not favor less productive businesses over more productive ones.
3. ***Simplicity:*** A fair tax should be simple. One frequent complaint about the federal income tax, often voiced around April 15, when taxes are due, is that the system is very complex, with forms that require many hours to complete. Increased complexity encourages people to make mistakes, promotes cheating, and builds resentment. Another example comes from residential property taxes. To figure a property tax, a government official must decide the value of a person's home. Formulas for assessing values vary widely, and the assessed values may or may not reflect the market values. This system can be very confusing to taxpayers.
4. ***Benefits received:*** A fair tax should tax individuals according to the benefits they receive from government services. Those who receive numerous benefits should pay more than those who receive few. For example, in some states, revenues generated from gasoline taxes are used to maintain and improve roads. Therefore, people who drive more pay more tax to support roads.

PART 2: APPLYING THE CRITERIA

Directions: Mark a plus or minus sign under each criterion to indicate whether the tax in question meets the criterion.

	Criteria			
Tax/Fee	**Ability to Pay**	**Efficiency**	**Simplicity**	**Benefits Received**
1. Driver's license fee (a fixed amount for each driver)				
2. Personal income tax (A percentage of wages and salaries up to a limit)				
3. Social Security tax (a percentage of wages and salaries up to a limit)				
4. Sales tax (a percentage of the pre-tax retail price of covered goods or services)				
5. Property tax (a percentage of the property's value)				

Unit 5, Lesson 29

Activity 2

The National Commission of Taxation Makes Its Annual Forecasts

WELCOME TO THE NCT

You have just been appointed by the President of the United States to the National Commission of Taxation (NCT). The purpose of the NCT is to forecast how changes in tax laws might change individual behavior. Every year, the NCT presents its forecasts to members of Congress and to the President for their consideration. And, every year, people are amazed at how well the NCT is able to predict changes in people's behavior.

BACKGROUND FOR NCT MEMBERS

There is a simple rule that guides the work of NCT members. They understand that taxes act as incentives. Changing the types of taxes levied and tax levels can influence people's behavior. Sometimes government deliberately raises or lowers taxes on particular goods and services to encourage or discourage certain types of behavior. For example, the first internal tax levied by the federal government was a tax on distilled spirits produced in the United States. This tax was justified not only as source of revenue but also as a way to discourage the use of alcohol. At other times, government leaders are not very certain about how changes in tax laws might change people's behavior. Ill-considered tax laws often result in unintended consequences.

A second rule is that there are substitutes for everything. If, for example, government makes one type of activity more expensive by increasing the tax on it, people often make substitutions. Applying this understanding has helped the NCT to predict actions that other government leaders had not considered.

YOUR JOB

Your job is to read each of the following situations and forecast how people's behavior might change. Form your response so that you identify what people might substitute in each case.

Situation 1: Congress increases the federal income tax by 25 percent for all income groups. How might individuals respond?

____

____

____

Situation 2: Your state raises the fee for a driver's license to $500 per person. How might individuals respond?

____

____

____

Situation 3: Complaints are increasing every year about tourists overcrowding the U.S. National Parks. The federal government increases the National Parks' camping fee to $50. How might individuals respond?

____

____

____

Situation 4: Freeways are very busy and travel is slow during morning and evening rush hours. The state government decides to make the freeways tollways during the peak hours (from 7:00 a.m. until 8:30 a.m. and from 4:00 p.m. until 5:30 p.m.) by imposing a $5.00 fee per car at each entrance ramp along the most-traveled 10-mile stretch of freeway. How might individuals respond?

____

____

____

Situation 5: Congress changes federal law so that homeowners are no longer permitted to deduct home mortgage interest from their taxable income. How might individuals respond?

____

____

____

UNIT 6

THE MACROECONOMY

Lesson 31

Activity 1 Solving the Labor Market Mystery

Lesson 32

Activity 1 Living with Inflation in the Former Soviet Union

Lesson 35

Activity 1 Fiscal Policy: A Two-Act Play

Lesson 37

Activity 1 Analyzing Diverse Viewpoints: Understanding Why Economists Disagree

Activity 2 Listening in on a Discussion of Economists

Activity 3 Sorting through Macroeconomic Theories

Lesson 38

Activity 1 Introducing Aggregate Demand

Activity 2 Introducing Aggregate Supply

Activity 3 The Effects of Shifts in Aggregate Demand and Supply

Activity 4 Economist for a Day

Unit 6, Lesson 31

Activity 1

Solving the Labor Market Mystery

The mystery in this case has to do with why the Bureau of Labor Statistics reports from time to time that the unemployment rate has increased at the same time that more people are getting jobs.

RECALL THE GUIDE TO ECONOMIC REASONING:

1. People choose.
2. People's choices involve costs.
3. People respond to incentives in predictable ways.
4. People create economic systems that influence individual choices and incentives
5. People gain when they trade voluntarily.
6. People's choices have consequences that lie in the future.

Now, let's consider the answers to the True/False questions.

A. Employed people are people with jobs.

The answer is *true*. The Bureau of Labor Statistics (BLS) is the federal agency in charge of measuring unemployment. The BLS conducts a monthly survey called the Current Population Survey (CPS) to measure unemployment in the country. The Bureau of Labor Statistics classifies people with jobs as employed. This may not be as obvious as it appears. For example, people are considered employed if they did any work at all for pay during the survey week. This includes all part-time and temporary work, as well as regular full-time, year-round employment. People also are counted as employed if they have a job at which they did not work during the survey week because they were on vacation, ill, experiencing child-care problems, and so forth.

B. Unemployed people are people without jobs.

The answer is *false*. Individuals are classified as unemployed if they do not have a job, have actively looked for work in the prior four weeks, and are currently available for work. To be considered unemployed, a person must be in the labor force. In order to be in the labor force, a person must have a job or be looking for one.

C. The civilian labor force is the number of people aged 16 years and older who are not in the armed forces.

The answer is *false*. All members of the civilian non-institutional population are eligible for inclusion in the labor force. To be counted as in the labor force, individuals must be aged 16 years or over. They must also have a job or be actively looking for a job. The United States had a labor force of about 141 million people in 2000.

All others — those who have no job and are not looking for one — are counted as not in the labor force. Who is left out of the official labor force count? Individuals not in the labor force are people going to school or retired people. Family responsibilities may keep others out of the labor force. Still others have a physical or mental disability that prevents them from participating in labor force activities.

The labor force is not a fixed number of people. It increases as the population grows. It expands or contracts depending on how the economy changes and how these changes influence people's decisions. It also changes according to seasonal changes.

How is the unemployment rate calculated? The unemployment rate equals the total number of unemployed persons divided by the total number of people in the labor force.

SOLVING THE MYSTERY

Now let's address the mystery of why the Bureau of Labor Statistics sometimes reports that the unemployment rate has increased at the same time that more people are getting jobs. The answer is one part arithmetic and one part incentives.

In Situation 1, the economy has an unemployment rate of 4.2 percent. Here is the arithmetic:

$$\text{Unemployment Rate} = \frac{\text{6 million unemployed individuals}}{\text{140 million individuals in the civilian labor force}} = \text{4.2 percent unemployment}$$

In Situation 2, the economy is in the early stages in an expansion. Employers decide that it is in their best interest to hire additional workers. Word begins to spread that job opportunities are becoming more abundant. This change presents an incentive to people who are not currently in the labor force. These individuals now choose to enter the labor force. Here is the arithmetic:

$$\text{Unemployment Rate} = \frac{\text{7 million unemployed individuals}}{\text{150 million individuals in the civilian labor force}} = \text{4.6 percent unemployment}$$

continued on next page   

If the total number of individuals entering the civilian labor force increases more rapidly than the number of people obtaining jobs, both the unemployment rate and the number of people with jobs can increase.

QUESTIONS FOR DISCUSSION

A. What agency measures the unemployment rate?

____

____

____

B. Who gets classified as employed?

____

____

____

C. Who gets classified as being in the labor force?

____

____

____

D. How is the unemployment rate calculated?

____

____

____

E. How can the unemployment rate increase at the same time that employment is increasing?

____

____

____

Unit 6, Lesson 32

Activity 1

Living with Inflation in the Former Soviet Union: Stories from Teachers in 1998

1. UKRAINE
(1993 INFLATION RATE: 4,735 PERCENT)

Inflation undoubtedly is affecting the economy in Ukraine in a sad way. In the early 1990s, people did not expect to experience inflation, so their goals remained the same — to keep their money in the banks and to buy government bonds or insurance policies. But a period of change emerged, and with it the rise of prices and inflation. As long as the growth of wages kept up with the growth of prices, the purchasing power of citizens was maintained. But when prices went up more than wages, people lost in many ways.

Millions of people lost their savings in banks because the money wasn't worth anything anymore. People lost their faith in the banks. Banks and other financial institutions will be working hard for a long time, trying to regain the trust of the population. Banks are experimenting with different ways of attracting deposits, but they are not popular.

Inflation can be a winning instrument in the hands of those who know how to use it properly, at least at an appropriate time. Some of those who had access to credit and loans managed quite well. For example, one family took out a loan for building a home, built it relatively quickly, and was able to pay off the loan without any significant damage to the family finances. The salaries of the family members went up some, and the value of the house increased greatly. In a similar way, but on a much larger scale, powerful government figures were able to gain.

The main and most reliable way for people to protect themselves against inflation today is to buy hard currency, mostly U.S. dollars. The dollar holds its value because inflation is not high in the United States. Furthermore, many people don't have any choice but to buy goods and hoard them — to avoid paying higher prices in the future. Or people buy durable goods, such as electronics or furniture, and then sell them in the future. In times of inflation the goods go up in value, but money goes down in value.

2. RUSSIA
(1993 INFLATION RATE: 896 PERCENT)

On the surface everything is simple: inflated prices, not enough money to buy things. More money is needed, but it is not supplied. Thus, in an artificial way, inflation is kept partially under control.

How did the wealthy, the top 10-15 percent of the Russian population, cope with inflation? They invested in real estate and jewelry. They built cottages with two to three floors, the value of which was equivalent to five two-bedroom apartments. They bought apartments beyond Russian borders, built houses, and bought hard currency — usually dollars. Thus they were able to escape inflation. The prices of these things went up, and they didn't hold rubles that lost their value.

How did the other 85-90 percent of Russians cope with inflation? There was not enough income for the most basic needs. Why? Government enterprises in which the salaries were supposed to be 800-900 rubles in actuality only paid 50-100 rubles at a time. The rest was issued in the form of coupons for meals at the work cafeterias and fast passes for the public transportation. Government organizations paid salaries one-to-three months late. The question at the top was where to get money to pay government workers, including teachers. If the government printed more money, the inflation would only get worse.

What has happened due to inflation is that people find ways to avoid using money. In the last few years, due to privatization reforms, it is quite easy to gain land for personal use. If an individual was born in the countryside, he can be given land upon request, even if he has not lived there. Many have taken advantage of this opportunity and are now providing for their families by growing agricultural products. And sometimes payments are made between organizations and enterprises by exchanging goods and services rather than money. Agreements are made between banks and enterprises to pay the rents and utilities of employees without issuing cash directly to the workers.

Such are the ways in which we run away and hide from inflation.

continued on next page  

3. Estonia
(1993 inflation rate: 89 percent)

Since the end of 1980s and until 1992, inflation in Estonia was very high — reaching 500 percent per year. Before that pensioners (retirees) were putting money aside for future funerals, as is our custom, but during the period of high inflation these savings were brought to zero. During the period of high inflation Estonians greatly increased the reserves of cheese, canned meats, linens, etc. Many didn't even pay attention to the sizes of clothing, and people were buying children clothes for many years in advance. They knew that it was better to buy now, because prices would be higher in the future.

Those who had savings tried to exchange it into hard currency such as U.S. dollars or German marks, although our country had a shortage of it. These currencies were more stable and safer. There were many limitations on currency exchange operations. Only a few banks were exchanging rubles into hard currency, and these banks had very long lines. Those who had friends, relatives or other connections in these banks were able to protect themselves better from inflation.

In 1992, Estonia implemented monetary reform targeted at fighting inflation. People could exchange 2,000 Soviet rubles for 200 Estonian krons. This took all money reserves other than krons out of the economy.

4. Latvia
(1993 inflation rate: 109 percent)

Hyperinflation in Latvia happened in 1992. I was working at school and received my salary on a regular basis. Salaries in Latvia were indexed (adjusted for inflation) regularly to keep up with inflation, and thus I did not experience any significant losses from that.

My parents — pensioners [retirees] — lived in the countryside during the summer, and that is where all our relatives went for their vacations. They grew vegetables, marinated cucumbers, made jams, picked berries and mushrooms. Everyone was preparing supplies for winter. This summer activity was not affected by inflation because money was not involved. (But Latvians also grow food in the summer when there is not inflation, because money saved in this way can be used for other purposes. There is a saying that a real Latvian can't live without land and also, that having a good meal is essential for a real Latvian.)

During that time it was very difficult to save anything, even though the Baltija Bank was offering 120 percent in interest. I always tried to spend my money right after the payday because prices would be higher the more days you waited. It was not that easy, as it was difficult to tell which goods were expensive or cheap that day. It felt great to buy an item which grew in price the next day. My sister who earned considerably more than me tried to purchase dollars and save them, but even that was difficult to do because sometimes dollars were not accessible or it was difficult to assess the exchange rate.

5. Belarus
(1993 inflation rate: 1,188 percent)

In 1990, when Belarus was still part of the USSR, my parents kept their money in a savings account. They had 5,000 Russian rubles in their account. In the summer of 1990, my father feared that money would be devalued and prices would go up, so he removed his money from the bank and bought furniture for my house. He got me a kitchen set and furniture for my guest room. Five thousand rubles were enough for purchasing this furniture.

My account had 3,000 rubles at that time. I didn't remove them to purchase anything, although my father was trying to convince me to withdraw that money from the bank and to buy goods. Pretty soon I could only buy 1 kilogram of meat for my money.

With each year, inflation is growing in Belarus. My retired parents are forced to grow fruits and vegetables in their gardening lot and preserve them for the entire year. Because they cannot afford to buy meat, they are raising a pig. It is through their self-sustainable agricultural practices that they are surviving during inflation.

continued on next page  

6. MOLDOVA (1993 INFLATION RATE: 789 PERCENT)

In Soviet times my grandfather had a deposit of 5,000 rubles or $312.50. In 1993 the national currency, the Moldavian leu, was introduced, and the denomination was one leu for 1,000 rubles. Today due to inflation five leu are only equal to $1, so the total value of Grandfather's deposit decreased to $1. It is an example of the problem of taking no action with a bank deposit during inflation.

I had a deposit at the Saving Bank too. The total sum was 3,000 rubles or $187.50. After the introduction of the national currency I withdrew my money and purchased a small house near the river Dnestr. It is a very beautiful place situated 70 kilometers from Kishinay. I own this house today, and my family spends holidays there. In 1996 my friend purchased a house near my house, and the price of this house was $3,000. There is an obvious difference between $187.50 and $3,000, isn't there?

7. LITHUANIA (1993 INFLATION RATE: 390 PERCENT)

Inflation made many troubles for all Lithuanians, no matter rich or poor, and for my family as well. During Soviet times, my family was from the middle class with medium earnings. We had the opportunity to save some money. My mother thought about me and my future. She put some rubles in a savings account in our Saving Bank of the Lithuanian Republic every year from my birthday. It was an agreement that I should get 1,000 rubles on my wedding day. In the 1970s and 1980s, the sum of 1,000 rubles would be a very nice wedding gift from parents. However, I am 28 and I am not yet married. I will never get this gift, but not because I am not going to marry someone. I will not get the gift due to inflation. In terms of litas, the new Lithuanian currency, 1,000 rubles are worth nothing. Now, 10 years after Lithuania became independent from the Soviet Union, the government has started to compensate people for their lost savings, but the compensation is much less than the money lost.

In another way my mother was able to benefit from inflation. In 1990 under the Soviet system, cars and one-room apartments were given the same price. When Lithuania became independent my mother foresaw that property like houses or apartments would be worth more than cars. So she sold our car, a new one but a Soviet model, and bought a one-room apartment. Now the price of the apartment is more than 1,000 percent higher and worth much more than a car. So now I do have my own valuable property and that is a result of inflation, and because of my very clever mother.

8. ARMENIA (1993 INFLATION RATE: 3,732 PERCENT)

Naturally, the growth of inflation in Armenia is reflecting itself on the well being of individuals, and especially on those who work in the government sectors. In November of 1993, Armenia introduced a new national currency, the dram. The official exchange rate was announced relative to the dollar, which was 1 dollar = 14.4 drami. After one month, the rate dropped to 1 dollar = 350 drami. Currently, it's fluctuating between 500 drami to 550 drami per dollar. Many people made mistakes during 1993, when Soviet rubles were changed to drami. Those who left money in savings accounts suffered terribly. Our family also lost a great deal of money that way. For example, those who had 5,000 rubles in the bank before the exchange could have bought a car. After the exchange and the inflation that followed, they could only purchase one piroshki [a fried dumpling].

continued on next page

9. ALBANIA
(1993 INFLATION RATE: 85 PERCENT)

In Albania the change of the political system after 1990 led to many inflationary situations that are still going on. During 1990-92 prices went up drastically and in an uncontrolled way. Meanwhile, wages remained the same. Everyone knows that in our prior communist system the only sector was the state sector. Therefore during the transition many government enterprises shut down and many people remained jobless while prices increased 20-30 times. The population was desperate. Before the 1990s, a family who saved 10,000 lek could buy an apartment. Months later this money would only buy food for two or three months.

We had another inflationary period during which pyramid schemes boomed in Albania. Companies pretending to be investment companies borrowed money from the people and paid very high interest rates, about 20 to 25 percent per month. For a while, some people who loaned their money to these companies earned a big quantity of money. From the interest alone they could earn a sum 100 times more than an employee in the state sector or private sector. But it turned out that these companies were just setting up pyramid schemes, and the money they paid out was from new lenders, and not profits from investments. They were bound to fail. The government intervened and the companies were closed. The closure of these companies brought many social problems. People lost all their savings, or worse they lost even their houses. Those who were jobless remained without a bit of money and often tried to emigrate illegally many times.

10. ROMANIA
(1993 INFLATION RATE: 256 PERCENT)

In 1998, the inflation rate was 50.8 percent in Romania. All prices were going up, but the real wages of workers were going down. Officially the index of wages was only about 60 percent of the inflation rate. But beginning in September 1998, the government paid no indexation, which meant that the wages of government employees didn't go up at all. The situation is dramatic for people who are retired. Their pensions do not buy enough for all their expenses. A lot of old people are in this situation and need help from their children or from charity organizations. Many retired people are looking for extra jobs. Usually, women offer their services as housekeepers or baby sitters, and men as persons who can fix different things in a home.

We have to also mention some things about peoples' savings. Because the inflation rate is so high and wages so low there are only a few people who can save. Usually, the banks offer a high interest rate – approximately 50 percent (this is average) a year. But, even so, the population prefers to keep money not in our national currency, but in a stable currency – in U.S. dollars.

For people from Romania, sometimes it is cheaper to spend money in a foreign country such as Greece or Turkey. In these countries the prices are low and the services are good.

Unit 6, Lesson 35

Activity 1

Fiscal Policy: A Two-Act Play

Directions: Group members should choose parts and prepare a few lines to use in acting out the roles.

ACT 1

Expansionary Fiscal Policy: The Tax Cut

Location: Yourtown, U.S.A.

Time: In the near future, when you are adults in the workforce.

CHARACTERS AND DESCRIPTION OF ROLES:

Narrator/Economist: Opens Act 1 of the play. Announces that the economy is in a deep recession. GDP has decreased steadily during the past year, along with consumer spending and business investment. This has resulted in increased unemployment nationwide. People are calling for the government to do something to help the situation.

President of the U.S. (via radio broadcast): Announces that the tax cut to households and businesses she has been promising has been approved by the House and Senate, and will be put into effect immediately via tax-rebate checks. Tells listeners that the recession is, of course, not the fault of her political party, and that she firmly believes that the tax cut will help to stimulate the economy and create jobs.

House-husband (takes care of the children while his wife works outside the home): Is delighted to receive the tax-rebate check. Spends the money by putting it toward the down payment on a new car that the family desperately needs.

Car Salesperson: Notes that car sales have picked up, so incomes for car salespeople have increased. Will spend the increased income to buy a new computer for the office.

Computer Store Manager: Describes how computer sales have increased recently. Needs to hire more workers to handle the additional consumer demand.

Unemployed Computer Technician: Gets hired at the computer store, and is happy to be working again. Celebrates by taking the family out to dinner.

Restaurant Owner: Discusses how business at the restaurant has increased. The increased revenue, along with the tax cut to businesses, provides the incentive to expand the business by building more restaurants.

Laid-Off Construction Worker: Gets called back to work to build a new restaurant. Will use part of the income from the job to take a trip to Hawaii.

Narrator / Economist: Summarizes effects of tax cut by pointing out that it has encouraged consumer spending and business investment. As more money was spent, more goods and services were produced. GDP increased, and unemployment decreased.

ACT 2

Contractionary Fiscal Policy: The Decrease in Government Spending

Location: Yourtown, U.S.A.

Time: In the near future, when you are adults in the workforce.

CHARACTERS AND DESCRIPTION OF ROLES:

Narrator/Economist: Opens Act 2 of the play. Announces that the economy has experienced high and increasing demand-pull inflation for some time. Prices are increasing rapidly. People are calling for the government to do something to help the situation.

President of the U.S. (via radio broadcast): Announces that to cure the inflation, government spending will be decreased, in part by decreasing spending on aerospace and other government funded programs. This will decrease overall demand in the economy and take pressure off rising prices. Tells listeners that the inflation is, of course, not the fault of her political party, and that she firmly believes that the decrease in government spending will help to end inflation.

Aerospace Engineer: Gets laid off from government position. Accepts lower-paying position elsewhere. Due to decrease in pay, decides not to buy a new home for the time being.

Construction Worker in Housing Industry: Notes that new homes are not selling as fast as before; their prices are falling, and he is working fewer hours. His family can't afford to eat out as often as before.

Restaurant Owner: Comments that business has fallen, but also notes that supplies are getting cheaper and workers can be hired at lower salaries than before. Decides to decrease prices of restaurant meals to get customers to return. Decides not to buy a new computer at this time.

Computer Store Manager: Discusses how sales are down and inventories are up, but costs of supplies also appear to be falling. Lowers prices on computers in inventory to encourage sales.

continued on next page   

Computer Technician: Due to decreased revenues at computer store, loses overtime pay. Decides not to buy a new car until the prices of new cars fall as much as his pay.

New-Car Salesperson: Due to decreased prices of cars, her commissions on sales have fallen. Will tell her husband, who stays home with the kids, to cancel the trip to Hawaii until the prices fall enough for them to afford it. Notes that overall in the economy, prices are falling.

Narrator/Economist: Summarizes effects of government spending cut by pointing out that it has decreased overall demand in the economy, caused prices to fall, and the rate of inflation to slow. As spending decreased, incomes decreased and eventually prices decreased too.

Unit 6, Lesson 37

Activity 1

Analyzing Diverse Viewpoints: Understanding Why Economists Disagree

It is not unusual to find experts disagreeing with each other. Experts disagree over all sorts of matters — nuclear power, environmental protection, and who will win the Super Bowl. Why do experts disagree? How can the average person make sense out of the differing viewpoints and recommendations? Here are several important factors that often lead economists to different conclusions.

1. DIFFERENT TIME PERIODS

One economist might state that the present policy of the government will lead to inflation. Another might disagree. Both could be right if they are talking about the effects of the policy on inflation at different times — for example, six months from now as compared to two years from now.

2. DIFFERENT ASSUMPTIONS

Because an economy is a complex system, it is often hard to predict the effects of a particular policy or event. Therefore, in order to be able to make predictions, economists usually must hold certain assumptions (or beliefs). But economists often differ in their assumptions. For example, one economist might assume (or believe) that the federal budget deficit will become larger next year; another might not. These different assumptions could be the result of how much economic growth — and tax revenues and government spending — they assume (or believe) will take place.

3. DIFFERENT ECONOMIC THEORIES

Economists agree on many matters, such as, "If the price of beef goes up and nothing else changes, people will buy less beef." That is a prediction with which nearly all economists would agree because it rests on the generally accepted law of demand. However, economists have yet to settle a number of important questions, especially those concerning macroeconomics. Macroeconomics deals with the behavior of the economy as a whole, or large subdivisions of it, and how to influence that behavior. Economists have several different theories or explanations about what influences macroeconomic behavior. There are common elements to these theories, but each theory has a different perspective. There is nothing unique to economics about this. In physics, chemistry, and biology, there are also competing hypotheses. Physical and social scientists are constantly testing different theories.

4. DIFFERENT VALUES

Economics is concerned with explaining what is happening in the economy. It is also concerned with predictions. The economist should be able to say to the President or to Congress, "If you follow Policy One, then X, Y, and Z will happen. If you follow Policy Two, then Q, R, and S will happen. Pick the policy giving the results you like better." In practice, such statements by economists often contain more than analysis and the prediction of results. Their statements often recommend policies they like because the results agree with their own values — that is, the results are the ones they prefer. For example, some economists will recommend Policy One because X, Y, and Z will happen, and they favor achieving X, Y, and Z. Other economists will recommend Policy Two because they favor achieving results Q, R, and S. Such disagreements are basically about which outcomes are preferred by the economists. The economic policies recommended are determined by the preferred outcomes.

Unit 6, Lesson 37

Activity 2

Listening in on a Discussion of Economists

Four distinguished professors of economics are discussing current economic policy at a luncheon press conference attended by leading reporters of business news. Let's listen in.

Professor T.X. Cut:

"Let's separate issues. On the fiscal-policy side, this administration's budget proposal is not extravagant or inflationary. The tax cuts are partly balanced by spending cuts. With so many people still unemployed and so many factories still closed, a policy of this kind cannot rekindle inflation. The tax cuts will stimulate consumer spending, work effort, and business investment in an economy just emerging from a recession. We must let people keep the fruits of their labor and savings as incentives to produce and invest more. The spending cuts will prevent government from continuing to receive an ever-increasing portion of the nation's economic pie."

Professor U.R. Nutts:

"Excuse me, Dr. Cut. But that position makes little sense. First of all, let me say that this administration's tax cuts and spending cuts have been and are grossly unfair. The tax cuts have favored the rich, and the spending cuts have reduced programs that help maintain economic security for Americans with low incomes. The present deficit and those projected for the future are so large that they threaten our recovery from the recession. Here's why. All deficits must be paid for by government borrowing, and because the government is borrowing so much money, there is less available for consumers and businesses. With government borrowing now likely to increase, interest rates will rise, and that will reduce spending for houses and cars — and, in fact, spending on anything bought with a loan — as well as business investment that must be financed by borrowing. In other words, some important private borrowing will be 'crowded out.' Sometime next year, the recovery will therefore weaken, and we'll move back into recession. Taxes should be raised, especially on the wealthy, and at least some government programs that help low-income people should be restored to their original funding levels."

Professor E.Z. Money:

"Let me just comment, U.R., on your point about federal spending and borrowing 'crowding out' private consumer spending and business investment. This is where monetary policy comes in. The Federal Reserve must continue to allow relatively free expansion of money and credit. If the Fed makes more money available, there will be less pressure for interest rates to rise. We'll be able to sustain the recovery in housing, autos, and other sectors. And businesses will be able to get loans for investments at affordable interest rates. Continuing our economic growth by sustaining this recovery is the most important task we have before us. Increasing taxes now would only reduce total spending, and thus threaten the recovery."

Professor Fred Critic:

"Excuse me, Dr. Money. You forget that the expansion of the money supply we're currently witnessing is part of a long history of bungling by the monetary policy makers. Our most recent recession was brought on by the Fed's jamming on the monetary brakes by an abrupt reduction in the increase of the money supply in order to bring inflation under control. They overdid it, as they always do, and produced a recession. Now, they're overdoing it in the other direction, stepping on the monetary accelerator and increasing the money supply too rapidly. That will stimulate the economy all right, but in a year or two those actions will rekindle inflation. The Fed will then again jam on the monetary brakes and produce yet another recession. Everyone knows this. Interest rates right now are higher than they should be because everyone expects more inflation later. Only moderate growth in the money supply can bring interest rates down in the long run. The only way to get back on a long-term, stable economic growth path is to reduce money growth to a steady, predictable, non-inflationary level."

Moderator:

"Ladies and gentlemen, that's all the time we have. Let's give our distinguished panel a round of applause."

Directions

Assume that economists disagree for the following reasons:

1. Because they use different time periods as frames of reference.
2. Because they make different assumptions.
3. Because they have different theories about how the economy works.
4. Because they have different values and ideas about which economic goals are most important.

On the next page you will analyze each professor's comments using the four reasons stated above.

continued on next page   

Now analyze each professor's comments, using the following format:

Name of professor: ____________________

Major point: ____________________

____

Time period: ____________________

Assumptions: ____________________

____

Theoretical support: ____________________

____

____

____

Values: ____________________

____

____

____

Name of professor: ____________________

Major point: ____________________

____

Time period: ____________________

Assumptions: ____________________

____

Theoretical support: ____________________

____

____

____

Values: ____________________

____

____

____

continued on next page

Name of professor: ____________________

Major point: ____________________

____

Time period: ____________________

Assumptions: ____________________

____

Theoretical support: ____________________

____

____

____

Values: ____________________

____

____

____

Name of professor: ____________________

Major point: ____________________

____

Time period: ____________________

Assumptions: ____________________

____

Theoretical support: ____________________

____

____

____

Values: ____________________

____

____

____

Unit 6, Lesson 37

Activity 3

Sorting through Macroeconomic Theories

The following ideas relate to two economic theories. Your job is to match the idea with the theory. Sort through the ideas and classify them under these headings:

KEYNESIAN THEORY

NEW CLASSICAL THEORY

Enter the ideas in the lists to the right.

- Recessions and depressions occur because of too little aggregate demand.
- Monetary and fiscal policies are generally ineffective in managing the economy.
- Monetary and fiscal policies have some short-term effects but have little influence in the long run.
- Fool me once, shame on you. Fool me twice, shame on me.
- Government can and should play a positive role in managing the economy.
- That government that governs least governs best.
- Inflation is caused by the government increasing the money supply by more than 3 to 5 percent a year.
- Monetary policy works through interest rates.
- Fiscal policy is more effective than monetary policy.
- Taxes primarily affect people's incentives to save, work, and invest.
- It is important that government economic policies be clear and consistent.
- Government may not be able to completely control the economy, but it can make it better.
- Lowering taxes or increasing government spending affects aggregate demand.
- There is a trade-off between unemployment and inflation.

KEYNESIAN THEORY

1. ____________________
2. ____________________
3. ____________________
4. ____________________
5. ____________________
6. ____________________
7. ____________________

NEW CLASSICAL THEORY

1. ____________________
2. ____________________
3. ____________________
4. ____________________
5. ____________________
6. ____________________
7. ____________________

Unit 6, Lesson 38

Activity 1

Introducing Aggregate Demand

The aggregate demand (AD) curve shows the total amounts of goods and services that consumers, businesses, governments, and people in other countries will purchase at each and every price level. It represents all the demand in the economy.

The aggregate demand curve looks a lot like a demand curve for a single product. However, there are big differences. The vertical axis is labeled "Price Level." The price level is a measure of the average weighted price of all goods and services. An increase in the price level indicates inflation. A decrease in the price level indicates deflation.

The horizontal axis is labeled "Real GDP." It represents the value of all final goods and services produced, adjusted for inflation. Think of real GDP as the quantity of the nation's output.

The AD curve is downward-sloping. This means that consumers, businesses, governments, and people in foreign countries together will buy more goods and services at a lower price level than they will at a higher price level.

Shifts in Aggregate Demand

Shifts in aggregate demand show the effects of events and government policies on the price level and real GDP. Anything that causes an increase in consumer, business, or government spending, or in net exports, will increase AD. For example, higher incomes increase consumer spending and therefore increase AD. More business investment increases AD. Higher government spending increases AD. If U.S.-made goods and services become more desirable in other countries, AD increases. Anything that decreases consumer, business, or government spending, or net exports, will decrease AD. If higher taxes decrease people's net income, AD decreases. If business profits are down, businesses may invest less, and AD decreases. If government spending decreases, AD decreases. If U.S.-made goods and services are selling less in other countries, AD decreases. Expectations of change also affect AD. For example, if consumers feel there is going to be a recession soon, they may save more and spend less. This behavior decreases AD.

Analyzing events that affect aggregate demand is easy. The key is spending. Now see if you can analyze how events shift the AD curve.

For each situation described below, determine whether the event will increase or decrease AD. Start with AD curve *C*. If you think the first situation would increase AD, write "increase" and move to curve *D*. If you think the first situation would decrease AD, write "decrease" and move to curve *B*. Move only one curve at a time. Do not skip a curve even if you think the situation will cause a huge increase or decrease in AD. If you think an event will not cause AD to shift, write "no change." Do not go beyond the five curves. If you need to go beyond the five curves, you need to rethink your answer!

Shifts in Aggregate Demand

Price Level

A B C D E

Real GDP

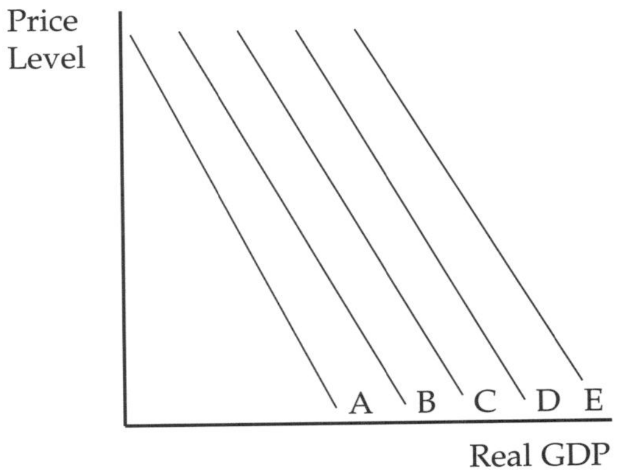

1. Congress cuts taxes.

   AD________________ Curve____________

2. A survey shows business investment spending decreased last month.

   AD________________ Curve____________

3. Government spending will increase next fiscal year; the President promises no increase in taxes.

   AD________________ Curve____________

4. A survey shows consumers are confident about the future economy.

   AD________________ Curve____________

5. Business leaders feel the economy is headed for recession.

   AD________________ Curve____________

6. The stock market collapses — investors lose billions.

   AD________________ Curve____________

7. Productivity rises for the fourth straight year.

   AD________________ Curve____________

8. The President cuts defense spending by 20 percent; there is no increase in domestic spending.

   AD________________ Curve____________

Unit 6, Lesson 38

Activity 2

Introducing Aggregate Supply

The aggregate supply (AS) curve shows the total amounts of goods and services that suppliers will produce at each and every price level. In the short run, the aggregate supply curve is upward-sloping. This means that during a period of a year or two, a higher price level increases the quantity of goods and services supplied. A decrease in the price level reduces the quantity of goods and services provided.

Economists and textbooks illustrate short-run aggregate supply in different ways. In general, short-run aggregate supply becomes more vertical at higher price levels. This is because at higher levels of real GDP, businesses have more difficulty in increasing their output even if the price level is higher.

Shifts in Aggregate Supply

Many events can shift short-run AS, but here is a simple way to analyze the effects of these events. Anything that changes production costs shifts aggregate supply. An increase in production costs decreases AS, and a decrease in production costs increases AS. For example, an increase in the price of oil would increase the cost of energy, an important production cost. This would decrease AS. An increase in productivity reduces the costs of production, which would increase AS.

Now see if you can analyze how events shift the AS curve. The key is whether the event increases or decreases the costs of production.

Shifts in Aggregate Supply

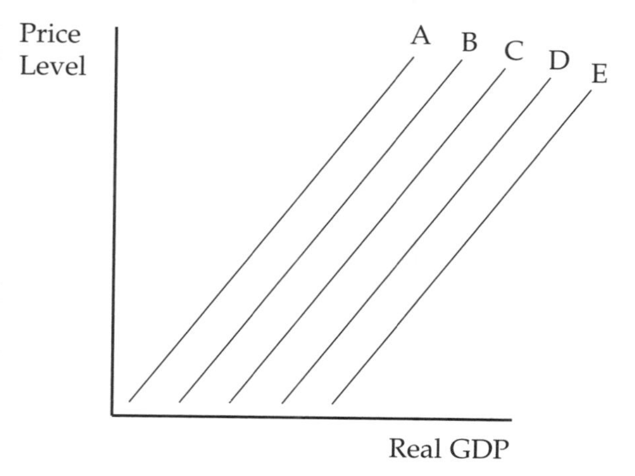

This Activity is similar to Activity 1, but it shows shifts in aggregate supply. For each situation described below, determine whether the event will increase or decrease AS. Start with AS curve *C*. If you think the first situation would increase AS, write "increase" and move to curve *D*. If you think the first situation would decrease AS, write "decrease" and move to curve *B*. Move only one curve at a time. Do not skip a curve even if you think the situation will cause a huge increase or decrease in AS. If you think a situation will not cause AS to shift, write "no change." Do not go beyond the five curves. If you need to go beyond the five curves, you should rethink your answer!

1. Unions grow more aggressive; wage rates increase.

   AS________________ Curve____________

2. OPEC successfully increases oil prices.

   AS________________ Curve____________

3. Labor productivity increases dramatically.

   AS________________ Curve____________

4. A giant natural gas discovery decreases energy prices.

   AS________________ Curve____________

5. Computer technology brings new efficiency to industry.

   AS________________ Curve____________

6. Government spending increases.

   AS________________ Curve____________

7. Cuts in tax rates increase incentives to work, save, and invest.

   AS________________ Curve____________

8. The low birth rate will decrease the labor force in the future.

   AS________________ Curve____________

9. Research shows that improved schools have increased the skills of American workers and managers.

   AS________________ Curve____________

Unit 6, Lesson 38

Activity 3

The Effects of Shifts in Aggregate Demand and Supply

When aggregate demand is equal to aggregate supply, the economy is in equilibrium. The equilibrium price level and the equilibrium real GDP are determined by the point at which the AD curve and AS curve intersect.

Shifts in AD and AS cause the equilibrium level of real GDP and the price level to change in the following ways:

- An increase in AD increases the price level and increases real GDP. There is a trade-off between higher inflation and higher GDP. During a recession, real GDP increases more than inflation. If the economy is near full employment, the price level will increase more than real GDP. Stimulating AD has different effects depending on whether the economy is in a recession or near full employment.
- A decrease in AD will decrease the price level and decrease real GDP. If the economy is in full employment, inflation will decrease more than real GDP. If there is a recession, real GDP will decrease more than the price level.
- An increase in AS decreases the price level and increases real GDP. This is the best of all possible situations — a lower price level, higher output, and less unemployment.
- A decrease in AS increases the price level and decreases real GDP. This is the worst of all possible situations — a higher price level, lower output, and higher unemployment.

For each of the four events below, make additions that illustrate the change on the diagram. Then indicate the response in terms of shifts in or movements along the AS curve or AD curve and the effect on real GDP and the price level in the short run. Indicate ***shifts*** in the curve by **S** and ***movements*** along the curve by **A**. Indicate the changes in the price level, unemployment and real GDP with (+) for an increase and (-) for a decrease.

	1. Increase in labor productivity due to technological change	2. Increase in the price of inputs used by many firms	3. Boom in investment, assuming some unemployed resources are available	4. A major reduction in investment spending
	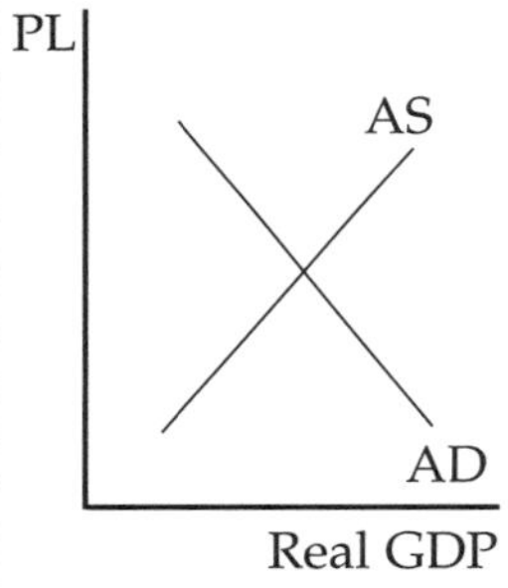 PL / AS / AD / Real GDP	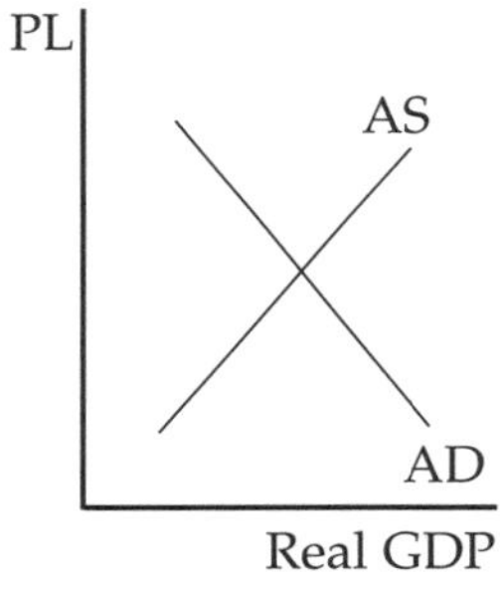 PL / AS / AD / Real GDP	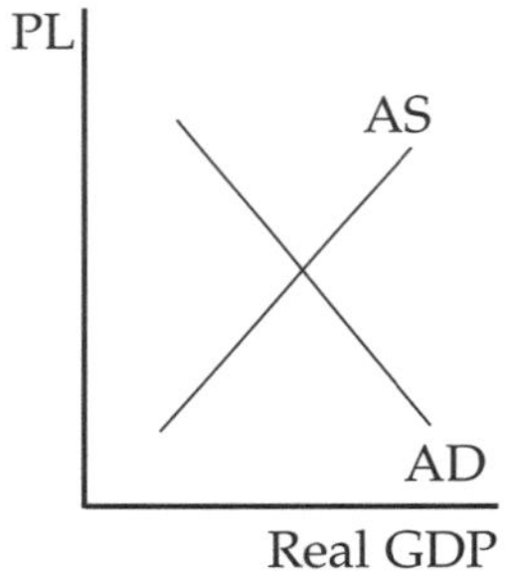 PL / AS / AD / Real GDP	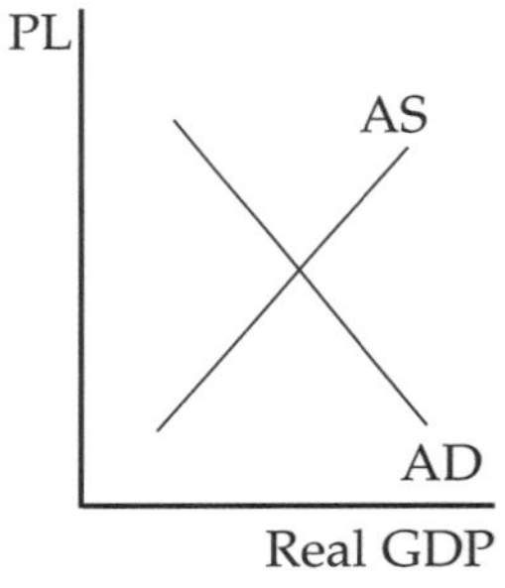 PL / AS / AD / Real GDP
AD curve				
AS curve				
Real GDP				
Price level				
Unemployment				

Unit 6, Lesson 38

Activity 4

Economist for a Day

Aggregate demand and aggregate supply are used to analyze the causes and effects of economic problems. Changes in aggregate demand and aggregate supply also provide guidance in analyzing the effects of government monetary and fiscal policies on inflation, unemployment, and economic growth. Understanding these macroeconomic forces helps you anticipate and respond intelligently to economic events. This allows you to predict the economic consequences of proposed government policies and to make informed choices among alternative political candidates and public-policy proposals.

Let's put on our economist hats and begin our analysis of the economy. For each situation described, illustrate the change on the AD/AS diagram and describe the effects on the equilibrium price level and real GDP by circling the correct arrow: (↑) for increase, (↓) for decrease and (–) for unchanged.

1. Increase in Government Spending

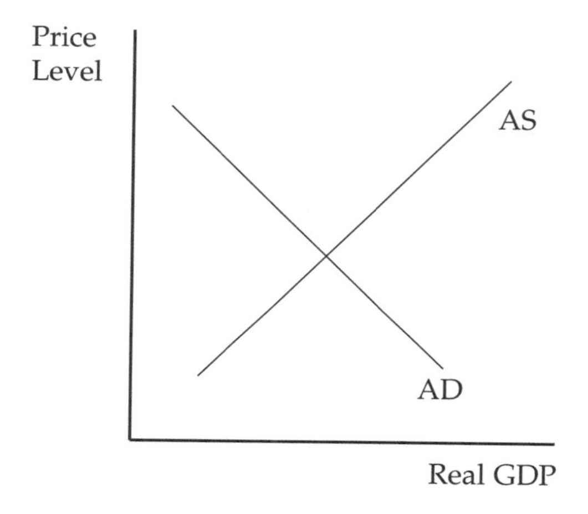

During a recession, the government increases spending on schools, highways, and other public works.

Price level ↑ ↓ –

Real GDP ↑ ↓ –

2. New Oil Discoveries

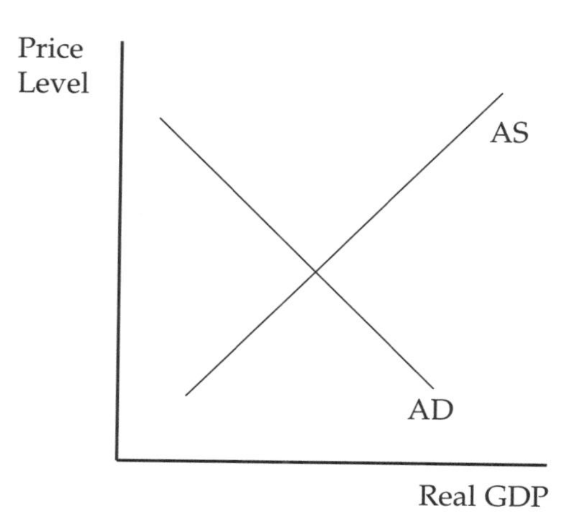

New oil discoveries cause large decreases in energy prices.

Price level ↑ ↓ –

Real GDP ↑ ↓ –

continued on next page  

3. Effects of New Technology and Better Education

Price Level

AS

AD

Real GDP

New technology and better education increase productivity.

Price level ↑ ↓ –

Real GDP ↑ ↓ –

4. Increased Confidence for Future Economy

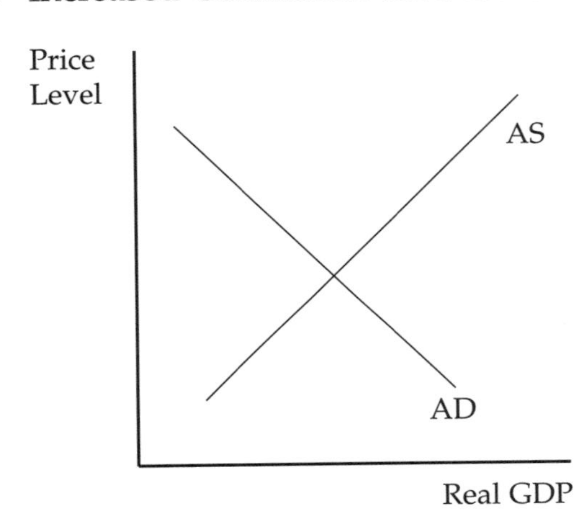

A new President makes consumers and businesses more confident about the future economy. *Note: Show the change in AD only.*

Price level ↑ ↓ –

Real GDP ↑ ↓ –

5. Income Tax Cut

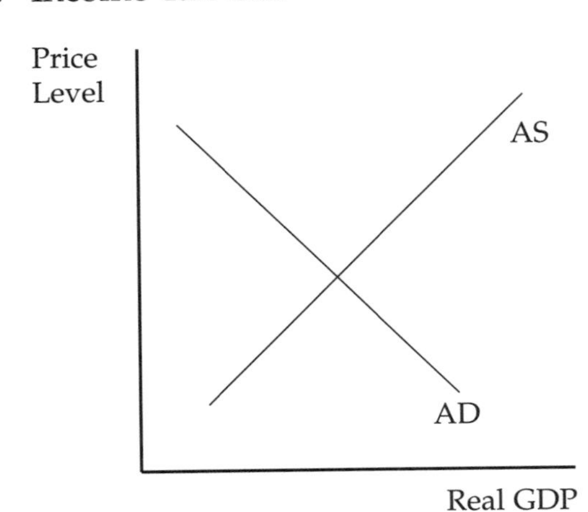

Congress passes a tax cut, and the President signs it.

Price level ↑ ↓ –

Real GDP ↑ ↓ –

UNIT 7

MARKETS WITHOUT BORDERS: THE GLOBAL ECONOMY

Lesson 39

Activity 1 Solving the Mystery of the Global Economy

Lesson 41

Activity 1 Why People and Nations Trade

Activity 2 Why Do People Buy Foreign Goods?

Activity 3 The Home-Building Mystery

Lesson 42

Activity 1 Foreign Currencies and Foreign Exchange

Lesson 43

Activity 1 Rich Nation / Poor Nation

Lesson 44

Activity 1 Environmental Case Studies

Activity 2 Environmental Policies

Lesson 45

Activity 1 Measuring Trade across Borders

Activity 2 How to Calculate the Current Account

Activity 3 U.S. Balance of Payments, 2000

Unit 7, Lesson 39

Activity 1

Solving the Mystery of the Global Economy

The mystery in this case has to do with why we seem focused on the global economy when it is a relatively small part of our total economy.

Recall the **Guide to Economic Reasoning**:

1. People choose.
2. People's choices involve costs.
3. People respond to incentives in predictable ways.
4. People create economic systems that influence individual choices and incentives
5. People gain when they trade voluntarily.
6. People's choices have consequences that lie in the future.

Now, let's consider the answers to the True/False questions.

A. The global economy is a growing part of the U.S. economy.

The answer is *true*. The U.S. economy is increasingly linked to the world economy. In 2000, international trade accounted for 26 percent of GDP. In 1975, however, it accounted for only 16 percent. While international trade does not account for most of U.S. GDP, it is clear that international trade is of growing importance.

Why are we going global? Decreasing costs are an important reason. For example, the cost of international telephone service per minute has fallen from $2.23 in 1975 to $0.45 in 2000. As a result, international telephone service has expanded rapidly. The Internet has also reduced communication costs. Similarly, the costs of transportation have fallen. Average freight costs for U.S. imports fell about 50 percent between 1975 and 2000. Faster delivery times, for example, have increased trade in perishable goods including fruit from Mexico, meat from Argentina, and eggs from New Zealand.

B. Some American workers benefit from international trade.

The answer is *true*. We often notice how American workers are harmed when plants close and jobs are moved to other nations. We are less likely to notice the new jobs for American workers that international trade creates. The global economy offers a market for goods and services produced by American workers. About 12 million American jobs are based on exports. Americans are heavily involved in exporting high-technology products of many sorts. American farmers also rely on sales to other nations. Exports of U.S. agricultural products were $53 billion in 2000. About 25 percent of cash sales by farms and ranches come from international sales. Exports also boost wages. Exporting businesses tend to pay higher wages than those that do not export. The potential of increased sales and income presents an important incentive to American workers and to American business.

C. American consumers benefit from international trade.

The answer is *true*. U.S. consumers are able to obtain goods and services from around the world. Americans do not have to consume only the products that can be produced within our borders. We have access to clothing, coffee, candies, fruit, electronics equipment and a long list of other products that are expensive or nearly impossible to produce here.

D. Prices in the United States are lower because of international trade.

The answer is *true*. Trade reduces the prices of some of the goods we consume. When a country is closed to trade, consumers can buy only goods and services produced within the nation's borders. This decreases competition for domestic businesses. Changing the rules of the economic system to permit trade presents an important incentive to business. Reducing trade barriers forces domestic businesses to compete on the basis of price as well as quality, to keep their customers happy. Increased competition from trade provides incentives for domestic businesses to produce at the lowest possible cost.

E. Trade barriers have been increasing around the world.

The answer is *false*. International organizations like NAFTA, the European Union, and the World Trade Organization have been leading the way to reducing trade barriers. Average tariffs on industrial goods have decreased steeply. Other barriers to trade including quotas and some regulations have also been reduced.

Why have we been changing the rules of international trade? Clearly, it is because people are better off as a result of increases in voluntary trade. The benefits we see in the United States--in expanded markets for workers, increased competition, and lower prices--are the same benefits that trade confers on our trade partners. For example, there is clear evidence that increasing trade leads to faster economic growth for developing countries. Nations that refuse to allow expanded trade may benefit a few privileged leaders at a cost to the nation's workers, consumers, and businesses.

continued on next page   

QUESTIONS FOR DISCUSSION

A. Why are we going global?

____

____

____

B. How do American workers and businesses benefit from international trade?

____

____

____

C. How do American consumers benefit from international trade?

____

____

____

E. How do our trade partners benefit from international trade?

____

____

____

F. Since international trade is a relatively small part of the American economy, why is there all the fuss about going global?

____

____

____

Unit 7, Lesson 41

Activity 1

Why People and Nations Trade

At first glance the answer to the question, "Why do people and nations trade?" seems to be "they want something they cannot produce themselves." For example, a trader might want commodities such as exotic fruit, spices, precious metals, and other natural resources. However, producers and consumers do not decide to engage in trade merely for goods or services they cannot produce for themselves. The fact is that countries whose citizens engage in international trade could produce much of what they import and, in many instances, have major domestic industries that do produce the same types of products they import. An obvious example of this in the United States is the importation of foreign steel, which competes with American-made steel.

A complete answer to the question, "Why do people trade?" is that international trade, like other voluntary exchanges, exists because both the buyer and the seller gain from it. If both parties did not expect to gain, there would be no trade between them.

If the decisions to buy foreign-produced products (such as cars, stereos, tin, and bananas), and to sell other products abroad (computer software, corn, and jeans), are viewed as *opportunities to gain*, we develop a more accurate perspective on the trade question. Every act of trade is undertaken because both the buyer and the seller think that they will gain from the trade.

Each trader — exporter and importer alike — responds to the positive incentive of gain. Consumers are not much different: they also respond to positive incentives. For buyers (importers), the positive incentive is to gain something by giving something else up — usually money. The gain comes because, from the exchange, they get something they value more — usually goods or services — than what they give up. Each time a purchase is made it is because the purchaser would rather have the good or service than the money. The same is true for the sellers (exporters) who gain by giving up a good or service to get something they would rather have — again, usually money. If both buyers and sellers, importers and exporters, get something of greater value than what they give up, then trade has made each of them better off.

The key to understanding the incentive to trade is to remember that people trade something they value less in order to gain something they value more. Notice how this incentive works in the trade of U.S. wheat for Honduran bananas.

U.S. farmers *could* grow bananas in greenhouses, yet the United States prefers to buy imported bananas. Why? The answer is obvious but important. To grow bananas, U.S. farmers would give up valuable land, time, and money to buy the necessary equipment and greenhouses. They gain more if they concentrate on wheat production. Their land and climate are better suited for growing wheat. Must America then go without bananas? Again, the answer is an obvious *no*. American farmers can sell wheat abroad for dollars and use some of these dollars to buy bananas grown by Hondurans in a climate and geographic setting well suited for growing bananas. In other words, either directly (by selling wheat to Honduras and using the dollars earned to buy bananas) or indirectly (by selling wheat to some other country and using the dollars to buy bananas grown in Honduras), Americans trade wheat grown in the United States for bananas grown in Honduras.

Applying the concept of opportunity cost to this trade, we can observe how total production increases when people specialize in the production of less costly goods and trade for products that would require a greater opportunity cost to produce at home (the principle of *comparative advantage*). Comparative advantage means having a relative cost advantage in the production of one type of good or service as compared to the production of some other good or service. This means that even if Country A can produce both of two different goods more cheaply than Country B can, it will still benefit A to specialize in the good which it can produce most cheaply, compared with another country. Country A will *export* that good to B and *import* the other good from B. From B's point of view, it is exporting the good which it can produce more cheaply and importing the other good. Thus both trading partners can gain if they specialize in the production of those things they produce at the lowest relative cost.

The ability to trade will also help to determine the set of products a nation or region can produce at the lowest cost. In the early 1800s, certain regions of the United States were probably best suited to specialize in grain production. Nevertheless, farmers had to be self-sufficient, and they produced many other products because relatively few opportunities for trade among the various regions existed. Only after the development of the railroads made it reasonably easy to transport goods throughout the United States did farmers begin to concentrate on producing the crops most efficiently grown in their region. The ability to trade has improved so much that many of today's U.S. businesses produce not only for domestic consumption, but for international trade as well. Soybeans in Illinois, lumber in Oregon, airplanes in Washington, and genetic technology in

continued on next page   

Massachusetts are all produced with the expectation that these products can be sold internationally.

Every time you buy a product that has been produced — even in part — in a foreign country, you send a message to importers in this country and exporters in other countries. The message is that you think you can gain by buying certain types of products produced in other countries. What was your incentive to buy the imported good? Why don't individuals make all the television sets, cars, shirts, or shoes they use? Or grow their own bananas? The decision of Americans to trade for these products illustrates that the concept of comparative advantage influences their economic choices.

QUESTIONS FOR DISCUSSION:

A. Why do people trade?

____

____

____

B. Why does the United States import bananas?

____

____

____

C. What is comparative advantage?

____

____

____

Unit 7, Lesson 41

Activity 2

Why Do People Buy Foreign Goods?

DIRECTIONS:

To learn why people participate in international trade, it is helpful to examine your own behavior and compare it to the behavior of other people. In this activity, you are asked to explain an imaginary purchase. You are also asked to acquire some information from other people about their purchases. Finally, you are asked to analyze these behaviors to see if they are consistent with the idea that incentives influence trading decisions. Read each question in this activity carefully and attempt to answer each question completely.

THE PROBLEM

You have decided to buy some new shoes to wear to school. You want comfortable shoes that can be worn often in good weather and bad. You have $150 of your own savings to spend on these shoes. Looking in a few stores, you find three brands — all of a similar style and with the features that you like.

The prices are:

$85.99
$78.99
$70.99

Remember that all three pairs of shoes are of the same style and quality, and you like all three. On the basis of price only, which will you purchase?
Check one:

__________ $85.99

__________ $78.99

__________ $70.99

The shoes you are considering are produced in three different countries: France, the United States, and Korea. Now that you know where the shoes are produced, which brand would you purchase? Check one:

__________France

__________United States

__________Korea

Considering both the price and the country, which will you purchase? Check one:

__________France $85.99

__________United States $78.99

__________Korea $70.99

What was most important in your decision — price or place of origin? (Keep in mind the three shoes had the same style and quality features.)

____

SURVEY AND COMPARISON

Do you suppose people in your community purchase goods with the same motivations that influenced your selection? Conduct the following survey and compare the results to your behaviors.

- Pick one imported good in your home and ask your parents why they purchased that good. Was it price? Quality? Country of origin? Ask them if they felt they gained in buying the imported good instead of a similar product made in the United States.
- Interview a merchant in your community and ask if any imported goods are offered for sale. If so, ask why. Is it because of price? Quality? Country of origin? Ask the merchant if he or she gains by selling the imported good instead of selling only products made in the United States.
- After you complete your interviews, compare the reasons these people give for their actions with your reason to purchase the shoes. Are you and the other people responding to the same or different incentives?

Unit 7, Lesson 41

Activity 3

The Home-Building Mystery

This is the story of two carpenters. Both are independent individuals who like to do their own work and provide good houses for their customers. Firman is the faster builder. Given his available resources, in one month he can build four wood houses or two brick houses. Right now, he finds that about half of his customers like brick houses and the other half like wood houses, so he works four months building wood houses and eight months building brick houses.

The second carpenter is not as fast at building houses. Given her available resources, Brickstrom is limited to producing one brick house or one wood house per month. Her customers are similar to Firman's. She makes six wood houses and six brick houses per year because about half of her customers prefer each type.

One day Brickstrom approached Firman and said, "We are missing a great opportunity here. If you would spend more time making wood houses and I spent more time making brick houses, we both could end up with more houses to sell each year."

Firman replied, "I'm good at building, but your proposal escapes my logic. We both know I'm the faster builder. I can make wood houses four times faster than you and brick houses twice as fast as you. What do I get out this deal? I'm willing to think about it, but you have to make a pretty good case."

"Remember when we studied economics together in high school?" Brickstrom asked. "Do you remember the concepts of opportunity cost and comparative advantage?"

"Not really," Firman said.

"Well, consider this. Every time you build two brick houses, you give up the opportunity to make four wood houses, right? You can't build both types at the same time."

"You are right there," Firman said.

"But, when I build a brick house, I only give up one wood house, right? So it is more costly for you to build brick houses than it is for me. I have a comparative advantage building brick houses. They only cost me one wood house. You have a comparative advantage building wood houses. They only cost you one half of a brick house. You should spend more time making wood houses. That is what you do best. Making brick houses is slowing down your production. Tell you what. Next year you spend six months building wood houses and six month on brick houses. I'll spend 12 months making brick houses. At the end of the year, we will swap five of my brick houses for seven of your frame houses and we will both have more homes to sell."

"Whoa, slow down," said Firman. "You are going too fast for me. Put it down on the paper in black and white. Show me the math!"

Can you help Brickstrom demonstrate her idea to Firman? In the spaces provided below, fill in the blanks to show how many houses are produced. Remember, Firman can make four wood houses a month or two brick houses. Brickstrom can make one wood house or one brick house a month. They both want an equal number of brick and wood houses to sell to their customers.

Annual Output before Specialization

	Wood Houses	Brick Houses
Firman	__ (4 months work)	16 (8 months work)
Brickstrom	6 (6 months work)	__ (6 months work)
Total output	22 houses	22 houses

Annual Output after Specialization

	Wood Houses	Brick Houses
Firman	__ (6 months work)	12 (6 months work)
Brickstrom	0 (0 months work)	__ (12 months work)
Total output	24 houses	24 houses

"See," Brickstrom said. "When you spend more time doing what do you best, we end up producing two more wood houses and two more brick houses — without adding any new work time, no new workers, and no new tools."

"OK, I see that increase," Firman said. "Looks good to me, but now you have only brick houses to sell (12) and I have twice as many wood houses compared to brick houses to sell (24 vs. 12). I thought you said we were going to end up with half wood and half brick each."

"You are right," Brickstrom said. "We need to get back to 50 percent each for our sales. But it was important for you to see that by specializing we increased our production. That is the most important idea in this exercise. Our economics teacher called it the principle of comparative advantage."

She continued: "Now for the second, less important problem. How can we get to a situation where we both have half wood and half brick houses for sale? I suggest

continued on next page  

we swap seven of your wood houses for five of my brick houses. Then we both end up better than we were before we specialized, and we each have exactly the same number of brick and wood homes to sell."

"Seven of my wood houses for five of your brick? Sounds like a funny deal to me," Firman said. "Show me the math." She did.

Annual Output after Specialization and Trade

	Wood Houses	Brick Houses
Firman	24 (6 months work) - 7 = 17	12 (6 months work) + 5 = 17
Brickstrom	0 (0 months work) + 7 = 7	12 (12 months work) - 5 = 7
Total output	24 houses	24 houses

"Look at these results," Brickstrom said. "Compare them to the results in the first table, before we specialized. You end up with one extra wood house and one extra brick house — with no additional work. I also end up with one more wood house and one more brick house than before. We both gain! No one loses!"

"Well, I'm a believer," said Firman. "Good thing you remembered something from that economics course, partner!"

Unit 7, Lesson 42

Activity 1

Foreign Currencies and Foreign Exchange

Simone, a 21-year-old veteran vagabond, peered into her wallet. Next to her passport and train tickets was her money. She pulled out her collection of pounds, rubles, kroner, yen, pesos, and euros. Simone looked up, confused. She tried to remember how she came to possess these currencies.

Simone is not alone. The world of foreign currencies often seems confusing. Not only are many of the names unfamiliar, but some travelers also want to know what each is worth in terms of U.S. dollars.

Because all of these currencies are money, they all serve the same functions. Money is a medium of exchange, a store of value, and a measure of value. As a medium of exchange, money can be used to purchase goods and services. As a store of value, money can be saved to use in the future. As a measure of value, money allows us to express the price of things. We can say a car costs so many dollars while a DVD player costs many fewer dollars.

Now to a basic question. How do we know what a foreign exchange rate is? How much is any currency worth in terms of other currencies? The simple answer is that a currency is worth whatever people are willing to pay for it. This is a case of supply and demand interacting in a market to establish a price for currency. If there is little quantity demanded for the country's currency, or a great quantity available for foreigners to buy, the money will be worth less on the foreign exchange market. If there is a high quantity demanded or only a small quantity supplied, then it will be worth more on the foreign exchange market.

For example, when Americans increase their purchases of imports, more U.S. dollars are sent abroad or are exchanged for foreign currencies in order to pay for the imported goods. As the supply of dollars to foreigners increases, the dollar tends to be worth less in terms of other currencies. Under such conditions we say the dollar *depreciates*. The same general analysis holds true for the currencies of other nations. If a currency increases its worth in terms of other currencies, we say it *appreciates*.

Currency values are established (and exchanges of currencies occur) in foreign exchange markets. These markets exist at banks, at the offices of foreign exchange dealers, and other places where one country's currency or checks can be exchanged for those of another country. But the greatest amount of foreign exchange activity takes place by telephone, electronically, or by other rapid means of communication used by commercial banks, businesses, and others who deal in large amounts of foreign exchange.

Foreign exchange values can change every day — most days by small amounts; some days by enough to make a difference to the people or businesses that are *converting* (exchanging) one currency into another. In the longer run, changes of great magnitude can occur. In the 1990s the value of foreign currencies, in general, fell a great deal against the U.S. dollar. Looking at the situation the other way, the dollar rose a great deal against foreign currencies.

In the 21st century, it will be interesting to see if the U.S. dollar remains "strong" relative the other currencies. When the euro was introduced in January 1999, one U.S. dollar could only buy .90 of a euro. By 2002, the U.S. dollar could buy 1.10 euros. Yet, by 2003, the U.S. dollar could only buy .98 euro. Values have continued to change since then. As the euro becomes more popular as a currency, it may reverse this trend and become a currency demanded by more people and businesses. If that happens, we should expect to see the euro's value trend back to its original value against the U.S. dollar.

QUESTIONS FOR DISCUSSION

A. What are the three functions of money?

1. ______________________________

2. ______________________________

3. ______________________________

B. The value of any currency is determined by the ______________ of it and the __________for it.

C. When a currency decreases in value, we say it____________.

When a currency increases in value, we say it ______________.

D. What do we call the places or means of communication by which currencies are traded and the value of one country's currency is established in terms of other currencies?________________

E. Assume the United States produces new products that citizens of other countries buy in large quantities. All other things being equal, what will happen to the value of the U.S. dollar in terms of foreign currencies?____________

F. Assume the number of U.S. citizens traveling to foreign countries greatly increases. All other things being equal, what will happen to the value of the U.S. dollar in terms of foreign currencies?________

Unit 7, Lesson 43

Activity 1

Rich Nation/Poor Nation

Part 1. You are secret agents assigned to find out if a country is rich or poor. From the information provided below, identify each of the five countries listed. Jot down the country's name opposite each bold-face heading.

Country A ______________________________

Size: Three-tenths the size of the United States

Population: 37,000,000 (small for a nation this size)

Natural Resources: Rich resources with fertile land and minerals such as lead, zinc, tin, copper, iron ore, oil, and uranium

Country B ______________________________

Size: About the size of California

Population: 127,000,000

Natural Resources: Fish, no mineral resources

Country C ______________________________

Size: Twice the size of California

Population: Large population of 127,000,000

Natural Resources: Vast resources including oil, tin, iron ore, coal, limestone, lead, zinc, and natural gas

Country D ______________________________

Size: 1.8 times the size of the United States

Population: 145,000,000

Natural Resources: Vast resources with major deposits of oil, natural gas, coal, many strategic minerals, vast timber supplies

Country E______________________________

Size: 3.5 times larger than Washington, D.C.

Population: 4,000,000

Natural Resources: Fish, deepwater port

Part 2. Rank the five countries you have identified in order, with the richest country placed at "1" and the poorest country at "5." Write the letter of the country used in the list above and the name of country.

Richest ↑↓ **Poorest**

	Country Letter	Country Name
1.	________	________
2.	________	________
3.	________	________
4.	________	________
5.	________	________

Unit 7, Lesson 44

Activity 1

Environmental Case Studies

Many environmental problems are global in scope. They occur in many countries and influence people in different countries. The following reading deals with four problems — ocean fishing, rain forest trees in South America, African elephants, and rice.Your task is to see how these issues differ and what they have in common.

OCEAN FISHING

Fish populations are declining in all parts of the world. The Mediterranean Sea no longer supports many fishers. They travel to other parts of the world to fish. The huge populations of Atlantic and Pacific salmon in North America have declined to levels that put them on the Endangered Species List. Shrimp, swordfish, and halibut populations are much lower today than 10 years ago.

What has happened? People now eat more fish. They demand more fish in the marketplace. Fishers try to provide plenty of fish for sale. Fishers use radar, sonar, spotter planes, sea-surface observations from satellites, advanced fishing gear, onboard processing, and refrigeration to gather fish from the sea to sell in the marketplace.

Many immature fish are caught along with mature fish. The fisher retains all for later sale. Fish are not returned to the sea to grow larger. They would just be caught by some other fisher if the first one to catch the fish were to turn them loose.

Fish of all sizes have many uses. They can be used for commercial sale and for sports fishing. They can be conserved and used when they become mature. They can be used for food for chickens, farmed fish, and people.

What does the future look like for wild fish populations? It appears they will continue to decline although most people would prefer to see the fish populations increase.

RAIN FOREST TREES

Trees in the South American rain forest are important to everyone who draws a breath of air. People use oxygen to breathe and convert it into carbon dioxide. Plants convert that carbon dioxide back to oxygen, without which we could not survive in this atmosphere. Rain forest trees are the biggest producer of oxygen in the world. They provide an excellent source of carbon conversion. They also provide habitat for a large, diverse number of plants, insects, and animals. The trees are also used for lumber production. Rain forests have become a popular destination for adventure tourists. Yet, each year thousands of acres of forest are burned to provide land to Brazilian ranchers and poor farmers.

To poor farmers, the trees are not valuable. There are many trees and very little land available on which they can grow crops to feed their families. The farmers burn the trees to clear the land for crops. Ranchers also burn the trees. It allows them to gain more pasture to graze cattle herds that can be sold on the meat market. No one owns the rain forest. But when the trees are gone, people can legally claim the land as theirs if they continue to use it for farming or grazing. In fact, the Brazilian government will help pay the costs of farmers and ranchers who are converting the forest to agricultural land.

AFRICAN ELEPHANTS

Elephants in Kenya once numbered in the hundreds of thousands. Now their population has declined to less than 20,000. Poachers kill them and sell the ivory in their tusks on the illegal market for more money than the poachers could earn by working for several years at a different job. No one owns the elephants. Most live in or near national parks in Kenya.

Most villagers living near the elephants tend not to care for the beasts. They compare them to huge, gray rats. The elephants eat enormous amounts of food, have a tendency to trample the villagers' food gardens, destroy village crops, and drink precious water supplies. Villagers tend to ignore the activities of poachers.

Kenyans are not allowed to own elephants, to sell them, or to use them as farm animals. They also are not allowed to guide hunters to hunt the elephants or to take people on tours to observe the herds.

RICE

Rice is a grain that once grew wild in Asia. More than 4,000 years ago, farmers learned how to cultivate rice. It has since become the most important food in Asia. Farmers work hard to keep the plant healthy. They provide fertilizer to help it grow; they prevent weeds from overtaking its growing space. They wait until the rice plant is mature before they harvest it. They always save enough seeds to insure a crop for next year. Rice is rarely over-harvested or harvested when it is immature.

Farmers usually own the land the rice grows on, and they own the rice they grow. They sell it to other people to earn income to buy food and clothing for themselves. Most rice is used for food by humans or animals. It can be eaten fresh from the harvest or stored and used in the future. Today, people eat more rice than at any other time in history, and more rice is grown today than ever before.

continued on next page   

QUESTIONS FOR DISCUSSION

A. In which of these situations do people own the resource before it is harvested?

____

____

____

B. Which of these resources are scarce? Do people treat these resources as scarce?

____

____

____

C. Which resources are growing more abundant?

____

____

____

D. Which resources are growing less abundant?

____

____

____

Unit 7, Lesson 44

Activity 2

Environmental Policies

Directions: Read the following suggested policies. Use a check mark to identify the policies that provide the incentives necessary to encourage voluntary stewardship (care) of these resources.

1. Allow villagers near the elephants to sell hunting rights to a small number of elephants each year and to conduct tours for tourists interested in viewing elephants.
   Encourage voluntary stewardship?______________

2. Require all villagers to report the identity of elephant poachers. Failure to do so would result in a $100 fine.
   Encourage voluntary stewardship?______________

3. Allow a small number of fishers the right (a license) to harvest a percentage of the fish population each year (50 percent). No other fishers may fish in the waters. If the fish population increases, the licensed fishers are allowed to take more fish if the percentage taken remains the same as before.
   Encourage voluntary stewardship?______________

4. Require fishers to stop fishing for five years while the fish population increases.
   Encourage voluntary stewardship?______________

5. Pay farmers and ranchers more money than they currently earn to protect trees from being destroyed in the rain forest. Allow them to own the protected land and to use any native plants for food and medicine if the plants will naturally reproduce themselves each year.
   Encourage voluntary stewardship?______________

6. Station government armies all along the rain forest to prevent ranchers and farmers from burning the rain forest to create pasture and farm land.
   Encourage voluntary stewardship?______________

Unit 7, Lesson 45

Activity 1

Measuring Trade across Borders

Part 1: A Conversation about Trade Reports

Imagine that you are eating lunch at a posh Washington, D.C., restaurant. Seated at the next table are Ms. Deficit, a U.S. trade negotiator, and her German counterpart, Herr Plus. Let's listen in on their conversation as they discuss the trade problems of their respective countries.

Ms. Deficit: This imbalance in our trade cannot continue. If you look in the balance of payments account, it is obvious that we have a deficit in the current account. This balance of trade deficit in the current account has put many of our exporting companies out of business and is pushing the United States into a recession.

Herr Plus: My country agrees that the situation cannot continue. The surplus in Germany's balance of trade is raising the price of our imported goods, and we are exporting so many goods that the German people are left with fewer products at home.

Ms. Deficit: So we agree something needs to be done. But what? Some of our businesses are calling for higher tariffs, and others want us to drop the value of the dollar, but neither of those actions is an acceptable alternative to the President.

Herr Plus: We also could raise the value of our currency or further stimulate our economy, but either of those actions would surely cost the Chancellor his job.

Fortunately, the waiter arrives to take our order, sparing us the rest of their conversation. While our order is being prepared, let's investigate some of the ideas the two diplomats are discussing.

What are the balance of payments accounts? They are an accounting report of all the payment flows leaving and entering a country, whether from individuals, businesses, or governments. The U.S. Department of Commerce records all U.S. international transactions to help government officials as well as interested private citizens and businesses make informed decisions concerning world trade and finance.

These transactions are divided into two categories: those which give rise to an inflow of payments between residents of one country and the rest of the world (called credits), and those which give rise to an outflow of payments (called debits). Consider the export of an automobile from the United States to Germany. The German buyer will supply the exchange market with euros in order to acquire the United States dollars needed to pay the U.S. supplier. Likewise, a German tourist in the United States will supply euros to the currency market in order to buy dollars to pay bills in the United States. Both transactions are recorded as credits to the U.S. balance of payments because they lead to an inflow of payments to the United States.

If U.S. tourists plan to visit Germany, they must supply U.S. dollars to the currency market to acquire euros. A U.S. film buyer who wishes to acquire film rights to a German movie must supply U.S. dollars to the currency market to acquire euros. Both transactions are recorded as debit items in the U.S. balance of payments because they lead to an outflow of payments from the United States.

Part 2: The Conversation Continues

Your food has arrived and your interest in the nearby conversation at the nearby table has returned. Is the current account deficit a bad thing for the United States? Or is Germany's surplus a bad thing for Germany? Here we must investigate a bit further. Ah, Ms. Money has arrived to join the trade negotiators at the table next to us. Ms. Money is an international banker. Let's eavesdrop again and hear what she has to say.

Ms. Money: You two are missing half the story! If the United States is importing more than it is exporting, how can it pay for the imports? By definition, what is acquired in imports must be either paid for or owed. What you have been ignoring is the flow of monetary capital: the so-called "capital accounts."

Ms. Deficit: What has that got to do with this terrible deficit in the current account?

Herr Plus: Or our current account surplus?

Ms. Money: Let's consider your country's situation, Herr Plus. Your country is earning far more U.S. dollars on its exports than it is using for its imports. What is happening to all those funds? Or your country, Ms. Deficit? How is the United States paying for that excess of imports over exports?

Herr Plus: I see what you mean. Many of our banks have invested those dollars back in the U.S. banks and are earning interest on them. Other German companies are investing in buildings and other projects in the United States as well.

Ms. Deficit: And I believe we are also obtaining funds from your citizens who are buying U.S. Government bonds. This action helps to finance our government's budget deficit and helps keep our taxes down.

continued on next page   

Ms. Money: Correct. So now you understand that a current account deficit or surplus is simply a measure of the balance between the goods and services being exchanged; it does not tell us much about the total amount of currency changing hands. You both were talking about an "imbalance" of trade as if your exchanges were like a teeter-totter with a football player on one end and a ballerina on the other.

I think now you understand that every exchange is beneficial to both sides and that the perceived imbalance in trade is really balanced by other, perhaps less visible activities. If trade truly were imbalanced, like the teeter-totter, it would stop very quickly.

Thank goodness that misunderstanding is cleared up! Let's look more closely at the capital account.

Suppose the U.S. businesses borrow funds from Germany to finance imports which exceed exports of goods and services. Are the borrowed funds recorded as a credit or a debit item? To answer this question, it is easiest to think of the United States as an exporter of an IOU; and, like other exports, IOUs would be recorded as credits in the capital account. As before, this borrowing of funds would give rise to an inflow of payments to the United States, which was our definition of a credit. Likewise, if a U.S. bank lends money to a German investor to construct a new building, this action would lead to a debit in the capital account of the U.S. balance of payments because it give rise to an outflow of payments to Germany.

These two accounts, the current account and the capital account, almost completely record the flow of currency into and out of the United States. But, like any measure, they are not completely accurate. The accounts include a place for a "statistical discrepancy" to measure unrecorded transactions and other imperfections in the data, and another account, the "official reserve account," to measure movements of official intergovernmental settlements that do any "balancing" necessary during a given time.

QUESTIONS FOR DISCUSSION

A. Do you understand what a credit is? Which way does the payment of money flow?

____

____

____

B. Do you understand what a debit is? Which way does the payment of money flow?

____

____

____

C. All trades must involve payment of money. What is not counted in these reports?

____

____

____

D. How would these reports change if the flow of money from illegal drug sales were reported?

____

____

____

Unit 7, Lesson 45

Activity 2

How to Calculate the Current Account

Directions: Now it is your turn to record some international transactions. Record each of the transactions below in the respective balance of payments accounts of the United States and Germany. The first transaction has been done for you. Normally, Germany would record its accounts in terms of euros. For convenience, we record it here in terms of U.S. dollars.

	United States		Germany	
	Debit	**Credit**	**Debit**	**Credit**
U.S. company sells $1 million of steel to German builder.		$1 m	$1 m	
Bank of America pays $5 million in interest to German depositors.				
U. S. citizens spend $3 million on Mercedes automobiles.				
A U.S. firm receives a $2 million dividend on its German investments.				
German tourists spend $3 million in the United States, while American tourists spend $5 million in Germany.				
A German firm pays $1 million to a United States shipping line to transport a load of cars.				
U.S. exchange students spend $8 million for tuition at a German university.				
The German government buys a $10 million missile from the U.S. Army to improve German defenses.				
Total				

The transactions in the examples above are all recorded in the current account of the balance of payments, and are what most of us think of as exports and imports of goods and services. Notice that the United States has exported less than it has imported and is left with a deficit in its current account (debits exceed credits in respect to Germany). Germany is in exactly the opposite situation; it has a surplus in its current account in respect to the United States.

Unit 7, Lesson 45

Activity 3

U.S. Balance of Payments, 2000

Directions: An abridged version of the U.S. balance of payments accounts for a sample year is reproduced in the information below. Read this information carefully and use it to answer the questions that follow.

U.S. Balance of Payments Accounts
(All figures are reported in millions of dollars.)

Current account:	
Exports	$+358,498.00
Imports	- 461,191.00
Net Transfers[1]	-14,983.00
Balance on current account	$-117, 676.00
Capital account:	
New U.S. assets abroad (capital outflow)	$ -32,436.00
Net foreign assets in the U.S. (capital inflow)	+127,106.00
Balance on the capital account	$+94,670.00
Statistical discrepancy[2]	$23,006.00

QUESTIONS FOR DISCUSSION

A. Does the U.S. current account have a deficit or a surplus? How do you know?

B. Is the United States a net international borrower or a net international lender of money? How do you know?

C. Can the United States continue to run a current account deficit and continue to be a net international borrower? (Hint: consider who gains and who loses in any voluntary exchange between two parties.)

D. Add the totals in the various accounts to confirm that they "balance," since all exchanges must balance or trading would cease.

E. This information was taken from the *Statistical Abstract of the United States* and records what happened several years ago. Look up the information in the current *Statistical Abstract of the United States* (it is updated annually and monthly) to see if our international borrower status has changed.

(1) U.S. government military and economic aid in the form of grants, government and private pensions sent to persons residing abroad and charitable contributions by U.S. organizations and citizens.

(2) The balance of payments on the current account and the capital account should be in balance (i.e., their sum should equal zero); that is why this set of data is called a "balance of payments." If their sum does not equal zero, it follow that any difference from zero is a "statistical discrepancy," i.e., a result of unrecorded transactions, imperfect data, or unavoidable errors in collecting the data.

Absolute advantage The ability to produce more units of a good or service than some other producer, using the same quantity of resources. See also **Comparative advantage.**

Adaptive expectations Expectations about inflation or other economic events.

Aggregate demand A schedule (or graph) that shows the value of output (real GDP) that would be demanded at different price levels.

Aggregate supply A schedule (or graph) that shows the value of output (real GDP) that would be produced at different price levels. In the long run, the schedule shows a constant level of real GDP at all price levels, determined by the economy's productive capacity at full employment. In the short run, the aggregate supply schedule may show different levels of real GDP as the price level changes.

Alternative One of many courses of action that might be taken in a given situation.

Assumptions Beliefs or statements presupposed to be true.

Balance of payments The record of all transactions (in goods, services, physical and financial assets) between individuals, firms, and governments of one country with those in all other countries in a given year, expressed in monetary terms.

Balance of trade The part of a nation's balance of payments accounts that deals only with its imports and exports of goods (also called merchandise or "visibles"). When "invisibles," or services, are added to the balance of trade, the result is a nation's balance on the current account section of its balance of payments.

Barriers to entry Factors that restrict entry into an industry and give cost advantages to existing firms. Examples would include the large size of existing firms, control over an essential resource or information, and legal rights such as patents and licenses.

Barter Trading a good or service directly for another good or service, without using money or credit.

Benefit The advantage(s) of a particular course of action as measured by good feeling, dollars, or number of items.

Bond A contractual obligation to repay a specified amount of money in a specified amount of time, including a set rate of interest on the amount that is borrowed.

Budget An element of financial planning where all income is listed and compared to all expenditures. Often expenditure decisions need to be made to hold spending less than or equal to income.

Budget deficit Refers to national budgets; occurs when government spending is greater than government income from taxes and tariffs in a given year. A yearly deficit adds to the public debt.

Budget surplus Refers to national budgets; occurs when government income is greater than government spending in a given year.

Business cycles Fluctuations in the overall rate of national economic activity with alternating periods of expansion and contraction; these vary in duration and degrees of severity; usually measured by real gross domestic product (GDP).

Capital account Part of a nation's balance of payments accounts; records capital outflows — i.e., expenditures made by the nation's residents to purchase physical capital and financial assets from the residents of foreign nations; also records capital inflows — i.e., expenditures by residents of foreign nations to purchase physical capital and financial assets from residents of the nation in question.

Capital Resources and goods made and used to produce other goods and services. Examples include buildings, machinery, tools, and equipment.

Choice Course of action taken when faced with a set of alternatives.

Collusion An agreement between firms to fix prices or engage in other activities to restrict competition in an industry.

Command economy An economy in which most economic issues of production and distribution are resolved through central planning and control.

Comparative advantage The ability to produce a good or service at a lower opportunity cost than some other producer. This is the economic basis for specialization and trade. See also **Absolute advantage**.

Competition Attempts by two or more individuals or organizations to acquire the same goods, services, or productive and financial resources. Consumers compete with other consumers for goods and services. Producers compete with other producers for sales to consumers. See also **Market structure**.

Complements Goods and/or services that are often consumed together; e.g., left and right socks, or tennis rackets and tennis lessons.

Support for the development of this glossary was provided to the National Council on Economic Education by the United States Agency for International Development through the Eurasia Foundation.

Compound interest Interest that is earned not only on the principal but also on the interest already earned.

Consumer price index (CPI) A price index that measures the cost of a fixed basket of consumer goods and services and compares the cost of this basket in one time period with its cost in some base period. Changes in the CPI are used to measure inflation. See also **Implicit price deflator**.

Concentration ratio The percentage of total industry sales by the largest firms (generally four or eight) in an industry. The concentration ratio provides a measure of domination in an industry by a few firms and serves as a measure of whether an industry is an oligopoly.

Consumers People who use goods and services to satisfy their economic wants.

Consumer surplus The difference between the price a consumer would be willing to pay for a good or service and what that consumer actually has to pay.

Consumption Spending by households on goods and services.

Contractionary fiscal policy A decrease in government spending and/or an increase in taxes designed to decrease aggregate demand in the economy and control inflation.

Costs The disadvantages of a particular course of action as measured by bad feeling, dollars, or numbers of items.

Credit The opportunity to borrow money or to receive goods or services in return for a promise to pay later.

Crowding out Increased interest rates and decreased private investment caused by government borrowing.

Current account Part of a nation's balance of payments accounts; records exports and imports of goods and services, net investment income, and transfer payments with other countries.

Cyclical unemployment Unemployment caused by fluctuations in the overall rate of economic activity. See also **Business cycles**.

Debt Money owed to someone else. Also see **Debt for individual** and **National debt**.

Debt for individual Money a person owes to someone else, usually a financial institution.

Deficit See **Budget deficit**.

Deflation A sustained decrease in the average price level of all the goods and services produced in the economy.

Demand A schedule (or graph) showing how many units of a good or service buyers are willing and able to buy at all possible prices during a period of time.

Determinants of demand Factors other than the price that change (shift) the demand schedule, causing consumers to buy more or less at every price. Factors include income, number of consumers, preferences, and prices of related goods.

Determinants of supply Factors other than price that change (shift) the supply schedule, causing producers to supply more or less at every price. Factors include number of firms, production costs, and new technology.

Diminishing marginal utility A widely observed relationship in which the additional satisfaction (marginal utility) associated with consuming additional units of the same product in a given amount of time eventually declines.

Distribution The allocation or dividing up of the goods and services a society produces.

Division of labor An arrangement in which workers perform only one or a few steps in a larger production process (as when working on an assembly line).

Economics The study of how people, firms, and societies choose to use scarce resources.

Economic functions of government In a market economy, government agencies establish and maintain a legal system to regulate both commercial and social behavior, promote competition, respond to market failures by providing public goods and adjusting for externalities, redistribute income, and establish macroeconomic stabilization policies. To perform these functions, governments must shift resources from private uses by taxing and/or borrowing.

Economic growth An increase in real output as measured by real GDP or per capita real GDP.

Economic incentives Factors that motivate and influence the behavior of individuals and organizations, including firms and government agencies. Prices, profits, and losses are important economic incentives in a market economy.

Economic profit A firm's total revenue minus all explicit and implicit costs of production, including opportunity costs.

Economic system The institutional framework of formal and informal rules that a society uses to determine what to produce, how to produce, and how to distribute goods and services.

Economic wants Desires that can be satisfied by consuming a good or service.

Economizing behavior Considering the costs and benefits of various alternatives and choosing the one with the greatest net benefits.

Elasticity See **Price elasticity of demand, Price elasticity of supply.**

Employment rate The percentage of the total population aged 16 or over that is employed. See also **Unemployment rate**.

Entrepreneurship A characteristic of people who assume the risk of organizing productive resources to produce goods and services; a resource.

Equilibrium price The price at which the quantity demanded by buyers equals the quantity supplied by sellers; also called the market-clearing price.

Equilibrium quantity The quantity demanded and quantity supplied at the equilibrium or market-clearing price.

Exchange Trading a good or service for another good or service, or for money.

Exchange rate The price of one nation's currency in terms of another nation's currency.

Expansionary fiscal policy An increase in government spending and/or a decrease in taxes designed to increase aggregate demand in the economy, thus increasing real output and decreasing unemployment.

Exports Goods and services produced in one nation and sold to consumers in other nations.

Externalities Economic side effects or third-party effects, in which some of the benefits or costs associated with the production or consumption of a product affect someone other than the direct producer or consumer of the product. See also **Market failures**.

Federal Reserve The central bank of the United States. Its main function is controlling the money supply through monetary policy.

Financial planning Setting short-, medium-, and long-range goals; then collecting and analyzing income and expenditure information to determine how to meet one's goals.

Firms Economic units that demand productive resources from households and supply goods and services to households and government agencies.

Fiscal policy Changes in the expenditures or tax revenues of the federal government, undertaken to promote full employment, price stability, and reasonable rates of economic growth.

Fixed costs Costs of production that do not change as a firm's output level changes. See also **Variable costs**.

Foreign exchange market Market where demand for and supply of foreign currencies determines exchange rates.

Fractional reserve banking system Under such a system, banks are required to hold only a specified fraction of each depositor's money. The rest can be lent out, thus "creating money."

Free rider One who enjoys the benefits of a good or service without paying for it.

Future consequences Costs and/or benefits of a choice that will be paid or gained at a later time.

Goods Tangible objects that satisfy economic wants.

Government failure Policy and budget choices by government officials that result in inefficiency.

Government spending Spending by all levels of government on goods and services; includes categories like military, schools, and roads.

Gross domestic product (GDP) The market value of all final goods and services produced in a country in a calendar year. See also **Gross national product (GNP)**.

Gross national product (GNP) An alternative to **Gross domestic product (GDP)** as a measure of the value of final goods and services produced in one year. **GNP** measures the value of output produced by resources owned by a nation's residents, regardless of where the resources are located. **GDP** measures the value of output produced by the resources located in a nation, regardless of who owns the resources.

Heterogeneous products Products (goods or services) that are differentiated by real or imagined differences in quality or other features, such as color, taste, styling, warranties, or complementary services provided to those who buy the products. See also **Homogeneous products**.

Homogeneous products Products (goods or services) that are identical, with no differentiating features. See also **Heterogeneous products**.

Households Individuals and family units that buy goods and services (as consumers) and sell or rent productive resources (as resource owners).

Human capital The health, education, experience, training, and skills of people.

Hyperinflation A very rapid rise in the overall price level.

Imperfect competition Any market structure in which firms are not price takers, but instead must seek the price and output levels that maximize their profits. See also **Perfect competition**.

Implicit price deflator A price index that compares the prices of all the goods and services produced in the current-year gross domestic product (GDP) to the price levels that prevailed for those same goods and services in an earlier year or years. The implicit price deflator is used to adjust values of nominal or current-price GDP to obtain values for the real GDP. See also **Consumer price index**.

Imports Purchases of foreign goods and services; the opposite of **Exports**.

Incentive Any reward or benefit, such as money or good feeling, that motivates choices and behaviors.

Income Payments earned by households for selling or renting their productive resources. For example, workers receive wage or salary payments in exchange for their labor.

Income inequality The unequal distribution of an economy's total income among people or families.

Inflation A rise in the general or average price level of all the goods and services produced in an economy.

Interdependence A situation in which decisions made by one person affect decisions made by other people, or events in one part of the world or sector of the economy affect other parts of the world or other sectors of the economy.

Interest Payments for the use of real or financial capital over some period of time; paid by those who use the resources to those who own them, as in mortgage payments paid by a borrower to a lender.

Investment Purchase of capital goods (including machinery, technology, or new buildings) used to make consumer goods and services.

Invisible hand A figure of speech representing the idea that firms and individuals making decisions in their own self-interest will at the same time create economic order and promote society's interests; coined by Adam Smith.

Keynesian theory The macroeconomic theory holding that business cycles are caused by changes in aggregate demand and that such cycles can and should be influenced by fiscal and monetary policy undertaken to promote economic stability.

Labor The quantity and quality of human effort available to produce goods and services.

Labor force The people in a nation who are aged 16 or over and are employed or actively looking for work.

Land (or Natural resources) "Gifts of nature" that can be used to produce goods and services; for example, oceans, air, mineral deposits, virgin forests, and actual fields of land. When investments are made to improve fields of land or other natural resources, those resources become, in part, capital resources.

Law of diminishing marginal returns Describes a phenomenon observed in all short-run production processes, when at least one input (usually capital) is fixed. As more and more units of a variable input (usually labor) are added to the fixed input, the additional (marginal) output associated with each increase in units of the variable input will eventually decline. In other words, successive increases in a variable factor of production added to fixed factors of production will result in smaller increases in output.

Loanable funds market Market in which the supply and demand for money, in the form of bank deposits and loans, determine the interest rate.

Macroeconomic equilibrium The equilibrium level of output and the price level where aggregate demand equals aggregate supply.

Macroeconomics The study of economics concerned with the economy as a whole, involving aggregate demand, aggregate supply, and monetary and fiscal policy.

Marginal analysis A decision-making tool for comparing the additional or marginal benefits of a course of action to the additional or marginal costs.

Marginal benefit The additional gain from consuming or producing one more unit; can be measured in dollars or satisfaction.

Marginal cost The change in a producer's total cost when output is increased by one unit; can be measured in dollars or negative feeling.

Marginal revenue The change in a producer's total revenues when one additional unit of output is sold.

Market economy An economy that relies on a system of interdependent market prices to allocate goods, services, and productive resources and to coordinate the diverse plans of consumers and producers, all of them following their own self — interests.

Market failures The systematic overproduction or underproduction of some goods and services that would occur in an unregulated market system when problems such as public goods, externalities, or imperfect competition are present.

Markets Places, institutions, or technological arrangements where or by means of which goods or services are exchanged.

Market structure The degree of competition in a market, ranging from many buyers and sellers to few or even single buyers or sellers. See also **Competition**.

Microeconomics The study of economics concerned with individual units of the economy such as consumers and businesses and firms, including individual markets and specific prices for goods, services, and resources.

Monetarist theory A macroeconomic theory holding that the main cause of changes in the business cycle are changes in money supply.

Monetary policy Changes in the supply of money and the availability of credit initiated by a nation's central bank to promote price stability, full employment, and reasonable rates of economic growth.

Money Anything that is generally accepted as final payment for goods and services; serves as a medium of exchange, a store of value, and a unit of account; allows people to compare the relative economic value of different goods and services.

Money supply Narrowly defined by economists as currency in the hands of the public plus checking-type deposits; also called M1.

Monopoly A market structure in which a single seller produces or sells all the units of a good or service in a particular market, and where the barriers to new firms entering the market are very high.

Monopolistic competition A market structure in which slightly differentiated products are sold by a large number of relatively small producers, and where the barriers to new firms entering the market are low.

Multiplier effect The idea that a small increase in spending by consumers, businesses, or government can cause large changes in economic production. The multiplier also works in reverse when spending decreases.

National debt The total amount owed by the national government to those from whom it has borrowed to finance the accumulated difference between annual budget deficits and annual budget surpluses; also called public debt.

Natural resources See **Land**.

Net exports Exports minus imports.

New classical theory A macroeconomic theory holding that government policies will have a limited effect on the business cycle since individuals and firms will take government policies into account when making decisions.

Non-exclusion A property of certain goods and services such that (once the goods or services are provided) they cannot be denied to or withheld from people who have not paid for the goods or services; examples include street lights or national defense.

Non-price competition Competition by firms trying to attract customers by methods other than reducing prices; examples include advertising and promotional gifts.

Normal rate of profit Profits just high enough to compensate producers for the explicit and implicit costs (including opportunity costs) they incur in producing a particular good or service, without leading to any net entry or exit by producers in that market. Also called normal profits. Normal profits are an economic cost of production; they mark a point at which any lower level of profit would lead a producer to pursue some other use of his or her resources.

Oligopoly A market structure in which a few, relatively large firms account for all or most of the production or sales of a good or service in a particular market, and where barriers to new firms entering the market are very high. Some oligopolies produce homogeneous products; others produce heterogeneous products.

Opportunity cost The second-best alternative (or the value of that alternative) that must be given up when scarce resources are used for one purpose instead of another.

Perfect competition A market structure in which a large number of relatively small firms produce and sell identical products and where and there are no significant barriers to entry into or exit from the industry. Firms in perfect competition are price takers and in the long run will earn only normal profits. See also **Imperfect competition**.

Personal distribution of income A classification of the income received by individuals or families; shows the number of people in various income categories, ranging from those receiving the highest level of income to those receiving the lowest.

Poverty The state of being poor, variously defined. Sometimes defined relatively — by reference, for example, to the average household income in a nation or region. Sometimes defined absolutely — by reference, for example, to the income needed to provide for adequate food, housing, and clothing in a nation or region.

Price The amount of money that people pay when they buy a good or service; the amount they receive when they sell a good or service.

Price ceiling A legally established maximum price for a good or service. See also **Shortage.**

Price elasticity of demand The responsiveness of the quantity demanded of a good or service to changes in its price. The price elasticity of demand is the percentage change in quantity demanded divided by the percentage change in price.

Price elasticity of supply The responsiveness of the quantity demanded of a good or service to changes in its price. The price elasticity of supply is the percentage change in quantity supplied divided by the percentage change in price.

Price floor A legally established minimum price for a good or service. See also **Surplus**.

Price level The weighted average of the prices of all goods and services in an economy; used to calculate inflation. See also Consumer price index.

Private good A good that provides benefits only to the purchaser.

Producers People and firms that use resources to make goods and services.

Producer surplus The difference between what a supplier is paid for a good or service and what it costs to supply the good or service. Added to **Consumer surplus**, it provides a measure of the total economic benefit of a sale.

Production possibilities frontier A table or graph that shows the full employment capacity of an economy in the form of possible combinations of two goods, or two bundles of goods, that could be produced with a given amount of productive resources and level of technology.

Productivity A ratio of output (goods and services) per unit of input (factors of production) per unit of time.

Profit Income received for entrepreneurial skills and risk taking, calculated by subtracting all of a firm's explicit and implicit costs from its total revenues.

Property rights Legal protection for the boundaries and possession of property. Assigning of property rights to individuals, collectives, or governments will depend on the economic system.

Public-Choice analysis The study of decision making as it affects the organization and operation of government and other collective organizations. Involves the application of economic principles to political science topics.

Public goods Goods for which use by one person does not reduce the quantity of the good available for others to use, and for which consumption can not be limited to those who pay for the good. Lighthouses, streetlights, and national defense are examples of public goods.

Purchasing power The amount of goods and services that a monetary unit of income can buy.

Quantity demanded The amount of a good or service a consumer will buy at a given price in a given period of time.

Quantity supplied The amount of a good or service a producer will sell at a given price in a given period of time.

Quotas In international trade, limits on the quantity of a product that may be imported or exported, established by government laws or regulations; in command economies, more typically a production target assigned by government planning agencies to the producers of a good or service.

Rational expectations Expectations about the future rate of inflation or other economic events that people form using all available information, including predictions about the effect of present and future policy actions by the government.

Rational expectations theory A branch of New Classical theory which holds that firms and individuals have rational expectations about the economy and government policies and thus may pursue their own interests in such a way as to render those policies ineffective.

Rational ignorance A decision not to obtain information about political issues or candidates because the costs of doing so outweigh the benefits.

Real gross domestic product (GDP) GDP measured in dollars of constant purchasing power. The measure is obtained by adjusting nominal GDP (GDP measured in current prices) by an appropriate price index — usually the implicit price deflator. Often used as a measure of economic activity.

Real interest rates The nominal (posted) interest rate minus the rate of inflation.

Recession A decline in the rate of national economic activity, usually measured by a decline in real GDP for at least two consecutive quarters (i.e., six months).

Resources The three (or four) basic kinds of resources used to produce goods and services: land or natural resources, human resources (including labor and entrepreneurship), and capital.

Salaries Payments for labor resources; unlike wages, not explicitly based on the number of hours worked. See also **Wages**.

Savings Disposable income (income after taxes) minus consumption spending.

Scarcity The condition that exists when human wants exceed the capacity of available resources to satisfy those wants; also a situation in a resource has more than one valuable use. The problem of scarcity faces all individuals and organizations, including firms and government agencies.

Secondary effects Effects indirectly related to a course of action whose influence will only be seen or felt later in time.

Secured debt Credit with collateral (a house or a car, e.g.) for the lender.

Services Activities performed by people, firms, or government agencies to satisfy economic wants.

Shared consumption A property of a good or service such that it can be used by many without diminishing another's ability to consume the same good; examples include street lights or radio broadcasts.

Shortage The situation that results when the quantity demanded for a product exceeds the quantity supplied. Generally happens because the price of the product is below the market equilibrium price. See also **Price ceilings**.

Special Interest Group An organization of people with a particular legislative concern. They work together to gather information, lobby politicians, and publicize their concern.

Specialization A situation in which people produce a narrower range of goods and services than they consume. Specialization increases productivity; it also requires trade and it increases interdependence.

Substitute A good or service that may be used in place of another good or service; examples include tap water for bottled water (or vice versa) and movies for concerts (or vice versa).

Supply A schedule (or graph) showing how many units of a good or service producers are willing and able to sell at all possible prices during a period of time.

Supply-side fiscal policy Policy intended to increase an economy's productive capacity by shifting aggregate supply; e.g., a tax cut giving businesses an incentive to invest and expand.

Surplus The situation that results when the quantity supplied of a product exceeds the quantity demanded. Generally happens because the price of the product is above the market equilibrium price. See also **Price floors**.

Tariff A tax on an imported good or service.

Taxes Compulsory payments to governments by households and businesses.

Total cost All costs associated with producing a good or service; the sum of fixed costs plus variable costs.

Total revenue All money received from selling a good or service; the price times the quantity sold of each item.

Trade Voluntary exchange of goods and services for money or other goods and services.

Traditional economy An economy in which customs and habits from the past are used to resolve most economic issues of production and distribution.

Tragedy of the commons Overuse or misuse of a commonly-owned resource, such as public grazing land or fishing waters.

Transaction costs Costs associated with buying or selling goods and services that are not included in the money prices of those goods and services. Examples include obtaining information on prices and product quality, searching for sellers, and bargaining costs.

Transfer payments Payments for which no goods or services are provided in return. Examples of government transfer payments include social security payments and unemployment insurance payments.

Unemployment Unemployment exists when people who want to work in jobs they are qualified to do at current wage rates are not able to find jobs, or are waiting to begin a new job, or are actively looking for work but do not have the skills required to fill the jobs that are currently available.

Unemployment rate The percentage of the labor force that is unemployed. See also **Employment rate**.

Unsecured debt Debt without collateral; credit card debt, for example.

Utility An abstract measure of the satisfaction consumers derive from consuming goods, services, and leisure activities.

Variable costs Costs that change as a firm's level of output changes. See also **Fixed costs**.

Voluntary trade See **Trade**.

Wages Payments for labor services that are directly tied to time worked, or to the number of units of output produced. See also Salaries.